STUDY GUIDE

Leonard T. Malinowski

Intermediate Algebra for College Students

SECOND EDITION

Allen R. Angel

Monroe Community College

Prentice Hall
Englewood Cliffs, New Jersey 07632

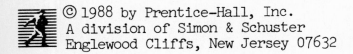 © 1988 by Prentice-Hall, Inc.
A division of Simon & Schuster
Englewood Cliffs, New Jersey 07632

Printed in the United States of America

10 9 8 7 6 5 4 3 2 1

ISBN 0-13-470071-6

Prentice-Hall International (UK) Limited, London
Prentice-Hall of Australia Pty. Limited, Sydney
Prentice-Hall Canada Inc., Toronto
Prentice-Hall Hispanoamericana, S.A., Mexico
Prentice-Hall of India Private Limited, New Delhi
Prentice-Hall of Japan, Inc., Tokyo
Simon & Schuster Asia Pte. Ltd., Singapore
Editora Prentice-Hall do Brasil, Ltda., Rio de Janeiro

Dedicated to Pat and Adam.

Contents

Chapter 3   Graphing Linear Equations

Chapter 4   Systems of Linear Equations and Inequalities

Chapter 5 Polynomials

Chapter 6 Factoring

Chapter 7 Rational Expressions and Equations

Chapter 8 Roots, Radicals and Complex Numbers

Chapter 9   Quadratic Equations and Inequalities

Chapter 10   Conic Sections

Chapter 11 Exponential and Logarithmic Functions

Chapter 12   Sequence, Series and Binomial Theorem

Acknowledgements:

Many people have contributed to the development of this supplemental text and should be recognized for their contributions. Allen Angel deserves my gratitude for his confidence in my work, and his support and encouragement.

Frank Mandery and Chris Bero, I owe my extreme gratitude for the amount of time they contributed to developing the final copy of the textbook. Frank Mandery helped brainstorm ideas for various sections of the book and helped proof drafts of the book. Chris Bero did an excellent job on the word processing from beginning data entry to final revision.

The Community College of the Finger Lakes deserves a special thanks for the use of the Micro-Computer Lab and the technical expertise of Mrs. Kay Carlisi.

Chapter 1   Basic Concepts

Section 1.1   Sets and the Real Number System

Summary:

A **set** is a collection of objects.

Set **A** is a **subset** of set **B**, written **A** ∈ **B**, if every element of set **A** is also an element of set **B**.

Example 1.   If the first set is a subject of the second set, insert ⊂ bewteen the two sets. If the first set is not a subset of the second set insert ⊄ between the two sets.

a.) {2, 4, 6, 8}   {0, 2, 4, 6, 8, 10}

b.) {1, 3, 5, 7, 9}   {1, 3, 5, 7, 11}

Solution: a.) {2, 4, 6, 8}   ⊂   {0, 2, 4, 6, 8, 10}

b.) {1, 3, 5, 7, 9} ⊄   {1, 3, 5, 7, 11}
because 9 is in the first set but not the second set.

Summary:

The **union** of set **A** and set **B**, written **A** U **B**, is the set of all elements belonging to either set **A** or set **B**.

The **intersection** of set **A** and set **B**, written **A** ∩ **B**, is the set of all elements common to both set **A** and set **B**.

Example 2.   Write A U B and A ∩ B if A = {1, 2, 3, 4, 5}
and B = {4, 5, 6, 7, 8}.

Solution: A U B = {1, 2, 3, 4, 5, 6, 7, 8}

A ∩ B = {4, 5}

Summary:

IMPORTANT SETS OF NUMBERS

Real Numbers $\{x \mid x \text{ is a point on the number line}\}$

Natural Numbers $\{1, 2, 3, 4, 5, \ldots\}$

Whole Numbers $\{0, 1, 2, 3, 4, 5, \ldots\}$

Integers $\{\ldots, -3, -2, -1, 0, 1, 2, 3, \ldots\}$

Rational Numbers $\left\{\dfrac{p}{q} \mid p \text{ and } q \text{ are integers, } q \neq 0\right\}$

Irrational Numbers $\{x \mid x \text{ is a real number that isn't rational}\}$

Every **rational number** when changed to a decimal number will
be either a repeating or a terminating decimal number.

Example 3.   State whether the following are rational or
irrational numbers.

a.) 8.54   b.) $\sqrt{6}$ c.) $\sqrt{64}$

Solution: a.) Rational

b.) Irrational

c.) $\sqrt{64} = 8$, Rational

-2-

Exercise Set 1.1

If the first set is a subset of the second set, insert $\subseteq$ between the two sets. Otherwise, insert $\not\subseteq$ between the two sets.

1.) {2, 5, 7}   {1, 2, 3, 4, 5, 6, 7}

2.) {3, 6, 9}   {3, 5, 7, 9}

3.) {2, 3, 5, 7}   {1, 2, 3, 4, 5, ...}

4.) {2, 4, 6, ...}   {1, 2, 3, 4, 5, 6}

Write the set of elements in A U B if:

5.) A = {2, 4, 5}   and   B = {1, 3, 6}

6.) A = {1, 5, 9}   and   B = {3, 6, 9}

7.) A = {5, 10, 15} and   B = {4, 8, 12}

8.) A = { }   and   B = {1, 2, 3, 4}

Write the set of elements in A ∩ B if:

9.) A = {2, 4, 5} and B = {1, 2, 5, 7}

10.) A = {5, 7, 9}   and B = {1, 3, 5, 7, 9}

11.) A = {1, 2, 3, 4, 5} and B = {5, 6, 7, 8, 9}

12.) A = {1, 3, 5, 7, 9, ...} and B = {2, 4, 6, 8, 10, ...}

State whether the following are rational or irrational numbers.

13.) 8.1643   14.) $\sqrt{49}$ 15.) $\sqrt{39}$

Solutions to Exercise Set 1.1

1.) $\subseteq$

2.) $\nsubseteq$

3.) $\subseteq$

4.) $\nsubseteq$

5.) {1, 2, 3, 4, 5, 6}

6.) {1, 3, 5, 6, 9}

7.) {4, 5, 8, 10, 12, 15}

8.) {1, 2, 3, 4}

9.) {2, 5}

10.) {5, 7, 9}

11.) {5}

12.) { }

13.) Rational

14.) Rational

15.) Irrational

Section 1.2   Properties of the Real Number System

Summary:

Properties of Real Numbers

For real numbers a, b, and c:

Addition	Multiplication

Commutative Property

$a + b = b + a$ $ab = ba$

Associative Property

$(a + b) + c = a + (b + c)$ $(ab)c = a(bc)$

Identity Property

$a + 0 = 0 + a = a$ $a \cdot 1 = 1 \cdot a = a$

Inverse Property

$a + (-a) = (-a) + a = 0$ $a \cdot \dfrac{1}{a} = \dfrac{1}{a} \cdot a = 1$

Distributive Property

$a(b + c) = ab + ac$

Example 1.   Name the property of real numbers.

a.) $6 + 4 = 4 + 6$

b.) $6(5) = (5)6$

c.) $(8 + 7) + 5 = 8 + (7 + 5)$

d.) $5(6 \cdot 8) = (5 \cdot 6)8$

Solution: a.) Commutative property of addition
                  b.) Commutative property of multiplication
                  c.) Associative property of addition
                  d.) Associative property of multiplication

Example 2.   Fill in the statement on the right side of the equal sign using the property indicated.

    a.) Commutative property of addition $6 + x =$

    b.) Distributive property $3(x + y) =$

    c.) Inverse property of multiplication $8 \cdot \dfrac{1}{8} =$

    d.) Inverse property of addition $x + (-x) =$

Solution: a.) $x + 6$ b.) $3x + 3y$

                  c.) 1 d.) 0

Example 3.   a.) What is the additive inverse of 7?

                  b.) What is the multiplication inverse of $\dfrac{6}{7}$?

Solution: a.) -7 b.) $\dfrac{7}{6}$

Summary:

For any Real Number a:

    Multiplication property of zero: $a \cdot 0 = 0 \cdot a = 0$

    Double negation property: $-(-a) = a$

Example 4.   Name the property

        a.) $8 \cdot 0 = 0$

        b.) $-\dfrac{-6}{7} = \dfrac{6}{7}$

        c.) $x \cdot 0 = 0$

        d.) $-(-b) = b$

Solution: a.)   Multiplication property of zero

        b.)   Double negation property

        c.)   Multiplication property of zero

        d.)   Double negation property

Exercise Set 1.2

Name the property.

1.) $6 + 0 = 6$ 2.) $4 + 5 = 5 + 4$

3.) $8 + (-8) = 0$ 4.) $0(7) = 0$

5.) $6 + (8 + 4) = (6 + 8) + 4$ 6.) $7 \cdot (4 \cdot 2) = (7 \cdot 4) \cdot 2$

7.) $8(x + 4) = 8(x) + 8(4)$ 8.) $-6 \cdot -1/6 = 1$

9.) $x \cdot 8 = 8 \cdot x$ 10.) $-(-7) = 7$

Fill in the statement on the right side of the equal sign using the property indicated.

11.) $2 + 7 = $ Commutative property of addition

12.) $6(8) = $ Commutative property of multiplication

13.) $4(0) = $ Multiplication property of zero

14.) $(5 + 6) + 3 = $ Associative property of addition

15.)   6(8 + 4) =   Distributive property

16.)   7 + (−7) =   Inverse property of addition

17.)   −(−8) =   Double negation property

18.) $12 \cdot \dfrac{1}{12}$ Inverse property of multiplication

19.)   7(x · y) =   Associative property of multiplication

20.)   (8 + x) + y =   Associative property of addition

Solution to Exercise Set 1.4

1.)   Identity property of addition

2.)   Commutative property of addition

3.)   Inverse property of addition

4.)   Multiplication property of zero

5.)   Associative property of addition

6.)   Associative property of multiplication

7.)   Distributive property

8.)   Inverse property of multiplication

9.)   Commutative property of multiplication

10.)   Double negation property

11.)   7 + 2   12.)   8(6)

13.)   0   14.)   5 + (6 + 3)

15.)   6(8) + 6(4)   16.)   0

17.)   8   18.)   1

19.)   (7x)y   20.)   8 + (x + y)

Section 1.3   Inequalities and Absolute Values

Summary:

Inequality Symbols

$>$ is read   "greater than"

$\geq$ is read   "greater than or equal to"

$<$ is read   "less than"

$\leq$ is read   "less than or equal to"

$\neq$ is read   "not equal to"

In a true inequality statement, the symbol $<$ or $>$ points to the smaller number, that is the one leftmost on a number line.

Example 1.   Insert $>$ or $<$ to make the statement true and draw a number line in each case.

        a.)   4   9

        b.)   7   2

        c.)   −3   −5

Solution: a.) 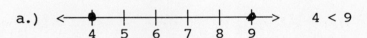   4 < 9

        b.) 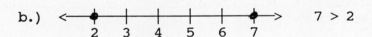   7 > 2

        c.) 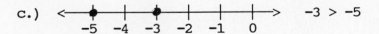   −3 > −5

Summary:

Absolute Value

If **a** represents any real number, then

$$|a| = \begin{cases} a \text{ if } a \geq 0 \\ -a \text{ if } a < 0 \end{cases}$$

Example 2.   Evaluate the expression.

a.) $|-7|$ b.) $-|8|$ c.) $-|-7|$

Solution: a.)   7   b.) $-(8) = -8$ c.) $-(7) = -7$

Example 3.   Insert >, < or = between the two numbers to make the statement true.

a.) $|9|$ $|-12|$

b.) $|-6|$ $|3|$

c.) $|-2|$ $-|-7|$

Solution: a.)   <   b.)   >   c.)   >

Exercise Set 1.3

Insert either < or > between the two numbers to make the statement true.

1.)   7   −2

2.)   −6   −2

3.)   −4   −7

4.)   6   8

5.) −41   −21

Evaluate the expression.

6.) $|-16|$

7.) $-|18|$

8.) $-|-18|$

9.) $|21|$

10.) $-|-21|$

Insert either >, < or = between the two numbers to make the statement true.

11.) $|-17|$ $|7|$

12.) $|4|$ $|-4|$

13.) $|-21|$ $|-25|$

14.) $|-111|$ $|-106|$

15.) $|-1|$ $-|-1|$

Solutions to Exercise Set 1.3

1.) >	2.) <	3.) >
4.) <	5.) <	6.) 16
7.) -18	8.) -18	9.) 21
10.) -21	11.) >	12.) =
13.) <	14.) >	15.) >

Section 1.4   Multiplication and Division of Real Numbers

To add two numbers with the same sign (both positive or both negative) add their absolute values and place the common sign before the sum.

Example 1.   Add a.)   5 + 7

                   b.)   −16 + −12

Solution: a.)   12

                   b.) $|-16|$ = 16

                         $|-12|$ = <u>12</u>

                                    28   Final answer is 28.

Summary:

To add two numbers with different signs (one positive and one negative) take the difference between the smaller absolute value and the larger absolute value. Place the sign of the larger absolute value before the answer.

Example 2.   Add a.)   −7 + 3

                   b.)   −13 + 18

Solution: a.) $|-7|$ = 7   7

                     $|3|$ = 3   <u>−3</u>

                                       4   Final answer is 4.

               b.) $|-13|$ = 13   18

                     $|18|$ = 18   <u>−13</u>

                                       5   Final answer is 5.

Summary:

To subtract **b** from **a**, add the opposite or additive inverse of **b** to **a**.

                   a − b = a + (−b)

Example 3.   Evaluate -8 - 10.

Solution: -8 + (-10) = -18

Example 4.   Evaluate 16 + (19 - (-2))

Solution: Remember operations within parentheses are done
              first.

              16 + (19 + 2) = 16 + 21 = 37

Summary:

The product of two numbers with like signs is a positive
number.

The product of two numbers with unlike signs is a
negative number.

The quotient of two numbers with like signs is a positive
number.

The quotient of two numbers with unlike signs is a
negative number.

Example 5.   Evaluate.

              a.)   -8(-7)

              b.)   (14)(-3)

              c.)   (-6) - (-2)

              d.) $\frac{-40}{8}$

Solution: a.) 56   b.) -42   c.) 3   d.) -5

Exercise Set 1.4

Evaluate.

1.) −3 + 6   2.) 9 + (−7)

3.) −14 + (−7)   4.) −31 + 18

5.) 7 − (−6)   6.) −18 − 7

7.) −4 − (−6)   8.) −31 − 17

9.) −12(4)   10.) 5(−11)

11.) (−12)(−3)   12.) (−7)(−7)

13.) −32 − (−4)   14.) −18 − 3

15.) −70 − (−5)   16.) 14 − (−2)

17.) 8 + (7 − 3)   18.) (4 − 2) + 6

19.) −6 − (−4 − 2)   20.) −18 + (4 −(−3))

Solution to Exercise Set 1.4

1.)   3   2.)   2   3.)   −21   4.)   −13

5.)   13   6.)   −25   7.)   2   8.)   −48

9.)   −48   10.)   −55   11.)   36   12.)   49

13.)   8   14.)   −6   15.)   14   16.)   −7

17.)   12   18.)   8   19.)   0   20.)   −11

Section 1.5   Exponents and Roots

Summary:

The number b to the nth power, written b^n, means

$$b^n = \underbrace{b \cdot b \cdot b \cdot b \cdot \ldots \cdot b}_{n \text{ factors of } b}$$

-14-

Example 1.   Evaluate.

a.) 7^2 b.) $(-4)^3$ c.) $\dfrac{2}{3}^{\,2}$ d.) $\dfrac{-3}{7}^{\,3}$

Solution: a.) $7^2 = 7 \cdot 7 = 49$

b.) $(-4)^3 = (-4)(-4)(-4) = -64$

c.) $\left(\dfrac{2}{3}\right)^2 = \dfrac{2}{3} \;\; \dfrac{2}{3} = \dfrac{4}{9}$

d.) $\left(\dfrac{-3}{7}\right)^3 = \dfrac{-3}{7} \;\; \dfrac{-3}{7} \;\; \dfrac{-3}{7} = \dfrac{-27}{343}$

Summary:

Any nonzero numbers, or letter, raised to the 0 power

has a value of 1. That is $a^0 = 1$ for $a \neq 0$.

A negative sign directly preceeding an expression that is
raised to a power has the effect of negating that expression.

Example 2.   Evaluate

a.) 6^0 b.) $4x^0$ c.) -5^0

d.) $(-3x)^0$ e.) $-(2)^4$ f.) $-(-5)^3$

Solution: a.) $6^0 = 1$

                b.) $4x^0 = 4(1) = 4$

                c.) $-5^0 = -(1) = -1$

                d.) $(-3x)^0 = 1$

                e.) $-(2)^4 = -16$

                f.) $-(-5)^3 = -(-125) = 125$

Example 3.   Evaluate $-(3)^4 - (-2)^3 + (-4)^2$.

Solution: $-(3)^4 - (-2)^3 + (-4)^2 = -81 - (-8) + 16$

                                        $= -81 + 8 + 16$

                                        $= -57$

Summary:
_____

The principal or positive square root of a number **n**,
written $\sqrt{n}$, is the positive number that when multiplied
by itself gives n.
_____

Example 4.   Evaluate.

                a.) $\sqrt{9}$ b.) $\sqrt{49}$ c.) $\sqrt{\dfrac{1}{9}}$ d.) $\sqrt{\dfrac{9}{16}}$

-16-

Solution: a.) $\sqrt{9} = 3$ since $3 \cdot 3 = 9$

b.) $\sqrt{49} = 7$ since $7 \cdot 7 = 49$

c.) $\sqrt{\dfrac{1}{9}} = \dfrac{1}{3}$ since $\dfrac{1}{3} \cdot \dfrac{1}{3} = \dfrac{1}{9}$

d.) $\sqrt{\dfrac{9}{16}} = \dfrac{3}{4}$ since $\dfrac{3}{4} \cdot \dfrac{3}{4} = \dfrac{9}{16}$

Summary:

The expression $\sqrt[m]{n}$ is read the mth root of n, and

$\sqrt[m]{n} = b$ if and only if $\underbrace{b \cdot b \cdot b \cdot \ \ldots \ \cdot b}_{\text{m factors}} = n$

Example 5.   Evaluate.

a.) $\sqrt[3]{8} = 2$ since $2 \cdot 2 \cdot 2 = 8$

b.) $\sqrt[5]{1} = 1$ since $1 \cdot 1 \cdot 1 \cdot 1 \cdot 1 = 1$

c.) $\sqrt[3]{-27} = -3$ since $(-3)(-3)(-3) = -27$

d.) $\sqrt[4]{\dfrac{16}{81}} = \dfrac{2}{3}$ since $\dfrac{2}{3} \cdot \dfrac{2}{3} \cdot \dfrac{2}{3} \cdot \dfrac{2}{3} = \dfrac{16}{81}$

Example 6.   Evaluate $3^2 + (-2)^3 - 4^2$.

Solution: $3^2 + (-2)^3 - 4^2 = 9 + (-8) - 16$

$= -15$

-17-

Exercise Set 1.5

Evaluate.

1.) 6^2 2.) 11^2

3.) $(-5)^3$ 4.) $(-2)^6$

5.) $\left(\dfrac{3}{4}\right)^3$ 6.) 8^0

7.) 8^0 8.) $12x^0$

9.) $-6x^0$ 10.) $(-4x)^0$

11.) $\sqrt{36}$ 12.) $\sqrt{144}$

13.) $\sqrt{\dfrac{1}{16}}$ 14.) $\sqrt{\dfrac{25}{16}}$

15.) $\sqrt{\dfrac{121}{144}}$ 16.) $\sqrt[3]{-64}$

17.) $\sqrt[5]{243}$ 18.) $\sqrt[3]{-1}$

19.) $\sqrt[3]{\dfrac{1}{64}}$ 20.) $\sqrt[3]{\dfrac{-125}{8}}$

Solution to Exercise Set 1.5

1.) 36   2.) 121   3.) −125   4.) 64

5.) $\dfrac{27}{64}$ 6.) 1   7.) −1   8.) 12

9.) −6   10.) 1   11.) 6   12.) 12

13.) $\dfrac{1}{4}$ 14.) $\dfrac{5}{4}$ 15.) $\dfrac{11}{12}$ 16.) −4

17.) 3   18.) −1   19.) $\dfrac{1}{4}$ 20.) $\dfrac{-5}{2}$

Section 1.6   Priority of Operations

Summary:

_____

To Evaluate Mathematical Expressions

Use the following order:

1. First, evaluate the information within parentheses,
    ( ), or brackets, [ ]. If the expression contains
    nested parentheses (one pair of parentheses within
    another pair), evaluate the information in the
    innermost parentheses first.

2. Next, evaluate all terms containing exponents and roots.

3. Next, evaluate all multiplications and divisions moving
    from left to right.

4. Finally, evaluate all additions and subtractions moving
    from left to right.

_____

Example 1.   Evaluate $8 + 3 \cdot 2$.

Solution: $8 + 3 \cdot 2 = 8 + 6$

$= 14$

Example 2.   Evaluate $3^2 - 4 \cdot 2 + 7 - 3 + 9$.

Solution: $3^2 - 4 \cdot 2 + 7 - 3 + 9 = 9 - 4 \cdot 2 + 7 - 3 + 9$

$= 9 - 8 + 7 - 3 + 9$

$= 14$

Example 3.   Evaluate $\left(\dfrac{2}{5} + \dfrac{3}{4}\right) \dfrac{1}{8}$

Solution: $\left(\dfrac{2}{5} + \dfrac{3}{4}\right) \dfrac{1}{8} = \left(\dfrac{8}{20} + \dfrac{15}{20}\right) \dfrac{1}{8}$

$= \left(\dfrac{23}{20}\right) \dfrac{1}{8}$

$= \dfrac{23}{160}$

Summary:

When evaluating expressions containing a fraction bar, work seperately above and below the fraction bar.

Example 4.   Evaluate $\dfrac{6^2 - 4 + 5(3)}{\sqrt{16} - 2 + 14}$

Solution: $\dfrac{6^2 - 4 + 5(3)}{\sqrt{16} - 2 + 14} = \dfrac{36 - 4 + 5(3)}{4 - 2 + 14}$

$= \dfrac{9 + 15}{2 + 14}$

$= \dfrac{24}{16}$

$= \dfrac{3}{2}$

Example 5.   Evaluate $3x^2 - 4y$ when $x = 5$ and $y = 7$.

Solution: $3x^2 - 4y = 3(5)^2 - 4(7)$

$= 3(25) - 4(7)$

$= 75 - 28$

$= 47$

Exercise Set 1.6

Evaluate.

1.) $15 + 4 \cdot 3$

2.) $4^2 - 5(2)$

3.) $3(5) - 4(6)$

4.) $(5 - 7)2 + 9$

5.) $\dfrac{3}{4} - \dfrac{1}{3} \cdot \dfrac{1}{2}$

6.) $\dfrac{3}{4}{}^2 - \dfrac{1}{16}$

7.) $16 - (8 - 2)$

8.) $2(4 - 1)^2 + 8$

9.) $\dfrac{5(7) - 3(4)}{12 + 4(7)}$

10.) $\dfrac{9 - 2^2}{7 - 11}$

11.) $\dfrac{\sqrt{25} - 3(2) + 8}{4^2 - 2(7) - 1}$

12.) $\dfrac{5(14 - 3) + 2}{6 - (4 + 7 \cdot 2)}$

Evaluate the following expressions when $x = 2$, $y = -3$, and $z = 4$.

13.) $3x + 7$

14.) $4y + 2x$

15.) $3x + 2z$

16.) $5y - 2z$

17.) $x^2 - y$

18.) $-y^2 + 3z$

19.) $4x^2 - 2y$

20.) $3x^2 - 2y + z$

Solutions to Exercise Set 1.6

1.) 27

2.) 6

3.) −9

4.) 5

5.) $\dfrac{7}{12}$

6.) $\dfrac{1}{2}$

7.) 4

8.) 26

9.) $\dfrac{23}{40}$

10.) $\dfrac{-5}{4}$

11.) 7

12.) $\dfrac{-57}{12}$

13.) 13

14.) −8

15.) 14

16.) −23

17.) 7

18.) 3

19.) 22

20.) 22

Practice Test

1.) Is {2, 4} ⊂ or ⊄ {0, 2, 4, 6, 8} ?

2.) Write the set of elements in A U B if A = {1, 13, 17} and B = {3, 11, 13, 14}.

3.) Write the set of elements in A ∩ B if A = {11, 12, 13, 14, 15} and B = {2, 3, 5, 7, 11, 13, 17, 19}.

4.) Is the $\sqrt{121}$ an irrational number?

5.) Is the $\sqrt{85}$ a real number?

Fill in the statement on the right hand side of the equal sign using the property indicated.

6.) 8(4) + 8(7)   =   Distributive property

7.) 13 + (x + z) =   Associative property of addition

8.) 19 + (−19)   =   Inverse property for addition

Insert > or < between the numbers to make the statement true.

9.) −61   − 56

10.) |−10| |3|

Evaluate.

11.) $-|-3|$

12.) −8 + (−13)

13.) (−7)(−8)

14.) $8^2 - 3(-2) + 5$

15.) $(-11x)^0$

16.) $\sqrt{\dfrac{16}{81}}$

17.) 12 − 4(−3)

18.) 21 − 3 + 7

19.) $4(8 - 3)^2 - 2$

20.) Evaluate $2x^3 - y$ when x = −4 and y = 12.

−22−

Solution to Practice Test

1.) $\subseteq$ 2.) {1, 3, 11, 13, 14, 17}

3.) {11, 13}   4.) No

5.) Yes   6.) 8(4 + 7)

7.) (13 + x) + z   8.) 0

9.) <   10.) >

11.) −3   12.) −21

13.) 56   14.) 75

15.) 1   16.) $\frac{4}{9}$

17.) 24   18.) 14

19.) 98   20.) −140

Chapter 2 Linear Equations and Inequalities

Section 2.1 Solving Linear Equations

Summary:

___

Properties of Equalities

For all real numbers **a**, **b**, and **c**.

1. $a = a$. **Reflexive property**

2. If $a = b$ then $b = a$. **Symmetric property**

3. If $a = b$ and $b = c$, then $a = c$. **Transitive property**

___

Example 1. Name the property indicated.

a.) $7 = 7$.

b.) If $y = 3$ then $3 = y$.

c.) If $x = 5$ and $5 = y$ then $x = y$.

Solution: a.) Reflexive property

b.) Symmetric property

c.) Transitive property

Summary:

Properties of Equalities (continued)

For any real numbers **a**, **b**, and **c**.

4. If $a = b$ then $a + c = b + c$.   **Addition property**

5. If $a = b$ then $a \cdot c = b \cdot c$.   **Multiplication property**

Since subtraction is defined in terms of addition, the addition property allows us to subtract the same quantity from both sides of an equation.

Also, since division is defined in terms of multiplication, the multiplication property allows us to divide both sides of an equation by the same **nonzero** number.

Example 2.   Name the property indicated.

  a.) If $x = 7$ then $x + 3 = 7 + 3$.

  b.) If $3x = 24$ then $\frac{1}{3}(3x) = \frac{1}{3}(24)$.

  c.) If $x = -5$ then $x - 2 = -5 - 2$.

  d.) If $\frac{1x}{4} = 8$ then $4(\frac{1x}{4}) = 4(8)$.

Solution: a.) Addition property

        b.) Multiplication property

        c.) Addition property

        d.) Multiplication property

Summary:
_____

The degree of a term is the sum of the exponents of the variables in the term.
_____

Example 3.   Give the degree of the term.

   a.) $4x^3$ b.) 5

   c.) $3x^2 2y^3$ d.) $\dfrac{2xy}{5}$

Solution: a.) Third   b.) Zero

            c.) Fifth   d.) Second

Summary:
_____

To Solve Linear Equations

1.   Eliminate all fractions by multiplying both sides of the equation by the least common denominator.

2.   Use the distributive property to remove any parentheses.

3.   Combine like terms on the same side of the equal sign.

4.   Use the addition property to rewrite the equation with all terms containing the variable on one side and all terms not containing the variable on the other side of the equal sign. It may be necessary to use the addition property a number of times to accomplish this. Repeated use of the addition property will eventually result in an equation of the form **ax = b.**

5.   Use the multiplication property to isolate the variable. This will give an answer of the form x = some number.

6.   Check the solution in the original equation.
_____

Example 4.   Solve each equation.

        a.) $3x + 5 = 92$

        b.) $3(2x + 5) = 39$

        c.) $\dfrac{4(x + 2)}{5} - \dfrac{1}{6} = \dfrac{47}{6}$

Solution: a.) $3x + 5 = 92$

      $3x + 5 - 5 = 92 - 5$ Addition property

              $3x = 87$ Combine like terms

         $\dfrac{1}{3}(3x) = \dfrac{1}{3}(87)$ Multiplication property

               $x = 29$ Simplify

Check: $3x + 5 = 92$

      $3(29) + 5 = 92$

        $87 + 5 = 92$

           $92 = 92$ True

    b.) $3(2x + 5) = 39$

         $6x + 15 = 39$ Distribution property

             $6x = 24$ Addition property

              $x = 4$ Multiplication property

Check:
$$3(2x + 5) = 39$$
$$3(2(4) + 5) = 39$$
$$3(8 + 5) = 39$$
$$3(13) = 39$$
$$39 = 39 \qquad \text{True}$$

c.)
$$\frac{4(x + 2)}{5} - \frac{1}{6} = \frac{47}{6}$$

$$30\left[\frac{4(x + 2)}{2} - \frac{1}{6}\right] = 30\left(\frac{47}{6}\right)$$

$6[4(x + 2)] - 5(1) = 5(47)$	Multiplication property.
$6[4x + 8] - 5(1) = 5(47)$	Distributive property.
$24x + 48 - 5(1) = 5(47)$	Distributive property.
$24x + 48 - 5 = 235$	Combine like terms.
$24x = 192$	Addition property.
$x = 8$	Multiplication property.

Summary:

Linear Equation Solutions

An identity is an equation that is true for all real numbers.
An inconsistent equation has no solution.
A conditional equation has one real number solution.

Example 5.   State whether each equation is inconsistent or
             an identity.

      a.) $5x + 4 = 2x + 3(x + 2)$

      b.) $7x - 9 = 3(x + 3) + 4x - 18$

      c.) $\dfrac{3x}{5} - 9 = \dfrac{x}{10} + 9 + \dfrac{x}{2}$

      d.) $\dfrac{x + 5}{9} = \dfrac{3x + 15}{27}$

Solution: a.) Inconsistent
             b.) Identity
             c.) Inconsistent
             d.) Identity

Exercise Set 2.1

Name the indicated property of equality.

1.) $8 = 8$

2.) $x + 7 = x + 7$

3.) If $x = -3$ then $-3 = x$

4.) If $a = 16$ and $16 = f$ then $a = f$

5.) If $x = -6$ then $x + 7 = -6 + 7$

6.) If $x = 3$ then $2x = 2(3)$

7.) If $x = 14$ then $\dfrac{x}{3} = \dfrac{14}{3}$

8.) If $x = -11$ then $x - 5 = -11 - 5$

9.) If $q = r$ then $r = q$

10.) If $r = s$ and $s = t$ then $r = t$

Give the degree of the term.

11.) $-4x^3y$ 12.) $5xyz$

State whether each equation is conditional, an identity or inconsistent. If the equation is conditional, solve for x.

13.) $x - 8 = 3x + 4$

14.) $15 = 3[7(x - 9) + 2]$

15.) $6 - (x - 8) = -4x + 3(x + 5) - 1$

16.) $\dfrac{4}{5}x - 5 = 5 + x$

17.) $8 = 2x - 2(x + 4)$

18.) $13 + 3x = 10 - (x - 3) + 4x$

19.) $7x - 9 = -7x - 9$

20.) $48 - 3x = 5(x + 2) - 8(x + 8)$

Solution to Exercise Set 2.1

1.) Reflexive property   2.) Reflexive property

3.) Symmetric property   4.) Transitive property

5.) Addition property   6.) Multiplication property

7.) Multiplication property   8.) Addition property

9.) Symmetric property   10.) Transitive property

11.) Fourth   12.) Third

13.) Conditional, $x = -6$ 14.) Conditional, $x = \dfrac{66}{7}$

15.) Identity   16.) Conditional, $x = -50$

17.) Inconsistent   18.) Identity

19.) Conditional, $x = 0$ 20.) Inconsistent

Section 2.2   Word Problems

Example 1.   For each of the following relationships, select a variable to represent one quantity and express the second quantity in terms of the first.

a.) Len is four years younger than Frank.

b.) An 8' board is cut into two pieces.

c.) It takes 30 minutes more to drive to Middlesex than to Canandaigua.

d.) The length of a rectangle is twice the width.

Solution: a.) Let x represent Frank's age in years.

Then x - 4 represents Len's age in years.

b.) Let x represent the length of the smaller board in feet.

Then 8 - x represents the length of the longer board in feet.

c.) Let t represent the time it takes to drive to Canandaigua in minutes.

Then t + 30 represents the time it takes to drive to Middlesex in minutes.

d.) Let w represent the width of the rectangle.

Then 2w represents the length of the rectangle.

Summary:

To Solve a Word Problem

1. Read the problem carefully.

2. Identify the quantity you are being asked to find.

3. Choose a variable to represent the quantity, and write down exactly what it represents.

4. Write the word problem as an equation.

5. Solve the equation for the unknown quantity.

6. Answer the question asked.

7. Check the solution in the original word problem.

Example 2. Five times a number plus 8 equals 88. Find the number.

Solution: Let N = the number
then 5N = five times the number

Five times the number + 8 = 88

$$5N + 8 = 88$$

$$5N = 80$$

$$N = 16$$

Check: $5(16) + 8 = 88$

$$80 + 8 = 88$$

$$88 = 88 \qquad \text{True}$$

Example 3.   The sum of two numbers is 51. Find the numbers
if one number is three more than twice the
other number.

Solution: Let x = the smaller number

then $2x + 3$ = the larger number

smaller number + larger number = 51

$$x \quad + \quad 2x + 3 \quad = 51$$

$$3x + 3 \quad = 51$$

$$3x \quad = 48$$

$$x \quad = 16$$

$$2x + 3 = 2(16) + 3$$

$$= 32 + 3$$

$$= 35$$

Check: $16 + 35 = 51$

$51 = 51$ True

Example 4.   Sherm is 11 years older than Frank. The sum of
their ages is 99.   Find Sherm's and Frank's
ages.

Solution: Let y = Frank's age in years
then $y + 11$ = Sherm's age in years.

Frank's age + Sherm's age = 99

$$y \quad + \quad y + 11 \quad = 99$$

$$2y + (?) \quad = 99$$

$$2y \quad = (?)$$

$$y \quad = (?)$$

Example 5.   The cost of renting a T.V. is $19.95 per month.
              If a new T.V. costs $399, how long would it
              take for the rental fee to equal the purchase
              price of the T.V.

Solution: Let M = number of months needed for the total
              rental fee to equal the purchase price of the
              T.V.

              Monthly rental fee · number of months = purchase
                                                        price

                    $19.95M = $399

                        M = 20

Check: $19.95(20) = $399

                  $399 = $399   True

Example 6.   Maine has a 5% sales tax. What is the maximum
              price of a car if the total cost including tax
              is $10,020.15.

Solution: Let x = total cost of the car.
              Then .05x = sales tax on the car.

                  Total cost + tax = Maximum cost

                    x + .05x = $10,020.15

                          1.05x = $10,020.15

                            x = $9543

Check: $9543 + .05($9543) = $10,020.15

              $9543 + $477.15 = $10,020.15

                $10,020.15 = $10,020.15   True

Exercise Set 2.2

Write the statement as an algebraic expression.

1.) Four times a number.
2.) Three more than a number.
3.) Eight more than twice a number.
4.) Six less than five times a number.

Select a variable to represent one quantity and express the second quantity in terms of the first.

5.) Ken is three times as old as Shawn.
6.) One number is 8 greater than another number.
7.) Two children share $5.
8.) One car travels 5 m.p.h. more than twice the speed of another.

Solve the following problems.

9.) One number is three times another number. If the sum of the numbers is 64, find the numbers.

10.) A number increased by 20% is 180. Find the number.

11.) Aimee's age is 1 year more than twice Zack's age. If the sum of their ages is 10 years, how old is each?

12.) Tim has $8 more than three times the money Luke has. Together Tim and Luke have $96. How much money does each one have?

13.) Mrs. Brown's company reimbursed her at 22 cents a mile whenever she used her own car for a business trip. If Mrs. Brown is to be reimbursed $69.30 for using her car on her last business trip, how far did she travel on the last business trip?

14.) To make a photocopy of a one page document costs a college student 10 cents. However, a student can buy a magnetic card for a $1 fee and will be charged only 7.5 cents for each photocopy made when using the magnetic card. How many photocopies must be made at the 10 cents rate to equal the cost of the magnetic card and photocopies made at 7.5 cents rate?

15.) The cost of a new carpet including sales tax is $490.06. If there is a 7% sales tax, then what was the cost of the carpet?

Solution to Exercise Set 2.2

1.) 4x   2.) x + 3

3.) 2x + 8   4.) 5x − 6

5.) Let x = Shawn's age,
     then 3x = Ken's age.

6.) Let x = the smaller number,
     then x + 8 = the larger number.

7.) Let x = money one child receives,
     then $5 − x = money the other child receives.

8.) Let x = the speed of the slower car,
     then 2x + 5 = the speed of the faster car.

9.) The smaller number is 16 and the larger number is 48.

10.) 150

11.) Aimee is 7 years old and Zack is 3 years old.

12.) Luke has $22 and Tim has $74.

13.) Mrs. Brown traveled 315 miles.

14.) 40 photocopies

15.) The carpet cost $458.

Section 2.3   Motion and Mixture Problems

Summary:

A formula with many useful applications is

$$\text{amount} = \text{rate} \cdot \text{time},$$

where the amount may be distance, length, area or volume.

Example 1. Tom, who works sealing driveways, can cover 350 square feet of driveway with sealer in 1 hour. What is the area of a driveway that Tom takes 3.25 hours to seal?

Solution: Area = rate · time

$$A = (350)(3.25)$$

$$A = 1137.5 \text{ square feet}$$

Example 2. Two cars leave at the same time traveling in opposite directions on Route 20. One car travels at 45 m.p.h. and the other car travels at 55 m.p.h. In how many hours will the cars be 450 miles apart on Route 20?

Solution:

Car	Rate	Time	distance
1	45	t	45t
2	55	t	55t

The sum of the distances is 450 miles. Thus,

distance car 1 + distance car 2 = 450

$$45t \quad + \quad 55t \qquad = 450$$

$$100t \qquad = 450$$

$$t \qquad = 4.5$$

In 4.5 hours the cars will be 450 miles apart.

Example 3.   Hunt's Dairy has 200 quarts of milk containing
5% butterfat. How many quarts of 2% butterfat
milk should be added to produce milk containing
4% butterfat?

Solution: Let x = number of quarts of whole milk to be
added.

Total butterfat in milk =
percentage of butterfat · amount of milk.

total butterfat + total butterfat = total butterfat
in 5% solution   in 2% solution   in 4% solution

$$0.05(200) \quad + \quad 0.02(x) \quad = 0.04(200 + x)$$

$$10 \quad + \quad 0.02x \quad = 8 + 0.04x$$

$$2 \quad = 0.02x$$

$$100 \quad = x$$

100 quarts of 2% butterfat milk must be added to
the 5% butterfat milk to obtain a 4% butterfat
milk solution.

Exercise Set 2.3

1.) Mr. Hopkins can type 85 words per minute. At that
rate, how long should it take him to type a 1,445
word document?

2.) Lisa can run one mile in 7 minutes and 28 seconds. How
much time would it take Lisa to run a 26 mile marathon
assuming she runs at the same rate?

3.) Two cars leave Portland at the same time and travel
south on Interstate 95. One car travels at 65 m.p.h.
and the other car travels at 57 m.p.h.   In how many
hours will the cars be 120 miles apart?

4.) Mrs. Ramano invests $12,000 for one year, part at 5.75%
and part at 8.25%. If she earns a total interest of
$902.50, how much was invested at each rate?

5.) Admission to a movie costs $5.75 for adults and $2.50 for children under twelve years of age. If 457 was the paid attendance at the movie and a total of $1652.75 was collected, how many adults attended the movie?

6.) Hi C is 10% fruit juice and Juicy Juice is 100% fruit juice. How much of each must be mixed to make 900 ounces of a party punch that is 50% fruit juice?

7.) Jelly filled donuts cost $1.92 a dozen (12 in a dozen), and cream filled donuts cost $2.28 a dozen. How many donuts of each type are in a dozen donuts that cost $2.13?

8.) Peanuts cost $.85 per pound and cashews cost $1.04 per pound. How much of each type of nut must be used to create a 39 pound mix of nuts worth a total of $36.00?

Solution to Exercise Set 2.3

1.) 17 minutes

2.) 11,648 seconds or 3 hours, 14 minutes, 8 seconds

3.) 15 hours

4.) $3,500 at 5.75% and $8500 at 8.25%

5.) 157 adults

6.) 500 ounces of Hi C and 400 ounces of Juicy Juice

7.) 5 jelly donuts and 7 cream donuts

8.) 24 pounds of peanuts and 15 pounds of cashews

Section 2.4   Formulas

Summary:

Literal Equations are equations that have more than one letter.

Formulas are literal equations that are used to represent a scientific or real-life principle in mathematical terms.

To solve for a given variable in a formula or equation it is necessary to get that variable all by itself on one side of the equal sign.

Example 1.   Solve for y: $3x - 8y = 24$ *question.*
                                            How was the answer
Solution: $3x - 8y = 24$ *derived?*

               $-8y = -3x + 24$

               $y = \dfrac{-3x + 24}{-8}$ *= 3 + 24 = $\dfrac{27}{-8}$ = 3x rem 3*

               $y = \dfrac{3x}{8} - 3$

Note: Formulas may use Greek letters.

Example 2.   Solve for w: $S = \dfrac{v\phi}{w}$

Solution: $S = \dfrac{V\phi}{w}$

               $Sw = V\phi$

               $w = \dfrac{V\phi}{S}$

-40-

Example 3.   Solve the m_1: $\dfrac{x}{5} = \dfrac{m_1}{m_1 - x}$

Solution: $\dfrac{x}{5} = \dfrac{m_1}{m_1 - x}$

$$x(m_1 - x) = 5m_1 \qquad \text{distributive property}$$

$$m_1 x - x^2 = 5m_1$$

$$-x^2 = 5m_1 - m_1 x$$

$$-x^2 = m_1(5 - x)$$

$$\dfrac{-x^2}{5 - x} = m_1$$

Exercise Set 2.4

Solve for the variable indicated.

1.) $4x + 2y = 18$, for y.

2.) $7x - 3y = 5$, for y.

3.) $C = 2\pi r$, for r.

4.) $V = \dfrac{1}{3}\pi r^2 h$, for h.

5.) $S = 2\pi r h$, for r.

6.) $A = \dfrac{1}{2}(b_1 + b_2)h$, for b_1.

7.) $F = k \cdot \dfrac{M_1 M_2}{d}$, for M_1.

8.) $\dfrac{Y_1}{x_1} = \dfrac{Y_2}{x_2}$, for Y_2.

9.) $A = P + PRT$, for P.

10.) $\dfrac{\alpha + \beta}{\Omega} = \sigma$, for β.

Solution to Exercise Set 2.4

1.) $y = 9 - 2x$

2.) $y = \dfrac{7x - 5}{3}$

3.) $r = \dfrac{C}{2\pi}$

4.) $h = \dfrac{3V}{\pi r^2}$

5.) $r = \dfrac{S}{2\pi h}$

6.) $b_1 = \dfrac{2A - b_2}{h}$

7.) $M_1 = \dfrac{dF}{kM_2}$

8.) $Y_2 = \dfrac{x_2 Y_1}{x_1}$

9.) $P = \dfrac{A}{1 + RT}$

10.) $B = \Omega\alpha - \alpha$

Section 2.5   **Solving Linear Inequalities**

Summary:

Properties Used to Solve Inequalities

1. If $a > b$ then $a + c > b + c$.

2. If $a > b$ then $a - c > b - c$.

3. If $a > b$ and $c > 0$, then $ac > bc$.

4. If $a > b$ and $c > 0$, then $\dfrac{a}{c} > \dfrac{b}{c}$.

5. If $a > b$ and $c < 0$, then $ac < bc$.

6. If $a > b$ and $c < 0$, then $\dfrac{a}{c} < \dfrac{b}{c}$.

Example 1.   Solve the inequality $3x - 6 > 18$, and graph the solution.

Solution: $3x - 6 > 18$

$3x - 6 + 6 > 18 + 6$

$3x > 24$

$\dfrac{3x}{3} > \dfrac{24}{3}$

$x > 8$

Graph
         8

-43-

Summary:

The solution set of an inequality graphed on the number line and written in interval notation.

Inequality	Graph	Iterval Notation
x > 3		(3, ∞)
x ≥ 3		[3, ∞)
x < 3		(-∞, 3)
x ≤ 3		(-∞, 3]
3 ≤ x < 5		[3, 5)
3 ≤ x ≤ 5		[3, 5]
3 < x < 5		(3, 5)

Example 2. Solve the following inequality and give the solution as a graph and in interval notation.

$$4(x - 3) \leq 3(x + 5)$$

Solution:

$$4(x - 3) \leq 3(x + 5)$$

$$4x - 12 \leq 3x + 15$$

$$x - 12 \leq 15$$

$$x \leq 27$$

Graph

Interval Notation (∞, 27]

-44-

Summary:

_____

To find the solution set to an inequality containing the word **and** take the **intersection** of the solution sets of the two inequalities.

_____

Example 3.   Solve $x + 5 > 7$ and $2x + 8 \leq 14$

Solution: Solve each inequality separately

$x + 5 > 7$ $\qquad\qquad$ $2x + 8 \leq 14$

$\qquad x > 2$ $\qquad\qquad\qquad$ $2x \leq 6$

$\qquad\qquad\qquad\qquad\qquad$ $x \leq 3$

Taking the intersection of the two sets. $\{x \mid x > 2\}$ and $\{x \mid x \leq 3\}$, we get the solution set $2 < x \leq 3$.

Summary:

_____

Continued inequalities are the form $a < x < b$. To solve a continued inequality, whatever we do to one part we must do to all three parts.

_____

Example 4.   Solve $3 < \dfrac{x + 7}{2} < 8$

Solution: $\qquad$ $3 < \dfrac{x + 7}{2} < 8$

$\qquad\qquad$ $6 < x + 7 < 16$

$\qquad\qquad$ $-1 < x < 9$

Summary:

To find the solution to an inequality containing the word or take the union of the solution sets of the two inequalities.

Example 5.   Solve $3x + 5 > 8$ or $2x + 7 < 3$

Solution: Solve each inequality separately.

$$3x + 5 > 8 \qquad\qquad 2x + 7 < -3$$

$$3x > 3 \qquad\qquad\qquad 2x < -10$$

$$x > 1 \qquad\qquad\qquad x < -5$$

Taking the union of the two sets $\{x \mid x > 1\}$ or $\{x \mid x < -5\}$, we get the solution $x < -5$ or $x > 1$.

Summary:

Phrases that represent inequalities:

Phrase	Meaning
x is at 12	$x \geq 12$
x is at most 12	$x \leq 12$
x is between 8 and 15	$8 < x < 15$
x is between 8 and 15 inclusively	$8 \leq x \leq 15$
x is no more than 12	$x \leq 12$
x is no less than 12	$x \geq 12$

Example 6.   If a canoeist can travel no more than 12 miles
               in $2\frac{1}{2}$ hours, at what rate of speed does she
               paddle the canoe?

Solution: Let x = the rate of speed of the canoe in mph.

$$12 \leq 2\frac{1}{2} \cdot x$$

$$4.8 \leq x$$

Exercise Set 2.5

Solve the inequality and graph the solution.

1.) $x + 7 \leq 13$

2.) $3x + 5 > x + 9$

Solve the inequality and write the solution in interval
notation.

3.) $5x - 3 \geq 9$

4.) $5(x - 1) < 4(2x + 5)$

Solve the following inequalities.

5.) $-1 < \dfrac{x + 4}{7} < 6$

6.) $2 \leq \dfrac{5 - 2x}{8} < 9$

7.) $2x + 5 \geq 15$ and $3x - 9 < 12$

8.) $4(x + 1) < 2x + 7$ and $5x - 9 < 21$

9.) $3x - 8 < 16$ or $x - 7 > 11$

10.) $12x - 9 \leq 3x + 9$ or $x + 9 \geq 12$

11.) John can run a mile in $8\frac{1}{2}$ minutes. How much time
      should John allow to run at least 5 miles?

12.) John can run a mile in $8\frac{1}{2}$ minutes. How much time
      should John allow to run between 8 and 12 miles?

Solution to Exercise Set 2.5

1.) $x \le 6$,

2.) $x > 2$,

3.) $x \ge 2.4$, $[2.4, \infty)$

4.) $-\dfrac{25}{3} < x$, $\left(-\dfrac{25}{3}, \infty\right)$

5.) $-11 < x < 38$, $(-11, 38)$

6.) $-33.5 < x \le -5.5$, $(-33.5, -5.5]$

7.) $5 \le x < 7$, $[5, 7)$

8.) $x < 1.5$ $(-\infty, 1.5)$

9.) $x < 8$ or $x > 18$ $(-\infty, 8) \cup (18, \infty)$

10.) $x \le 2$ or $x \ge 3$ $(-\infty, 2] \cup [3, \infty)$

11.) At least $42\frac{1}{2}$ minutes.

12.) Between 68 minutes to 102 minutes.

Section 2.6   Solving Equations and Inequalities Containing Absolute Values

Summary:

Procedures for Solving Equations and Inequalities Containing Absolute Value

For $a > 0$

1. if $|x| = a$ then $x = a$ or $x = -a$.

2. if $|x| < a$ then $-a < x < a$.

3. if $|x| > a$ then $x < -a$ or $x > a$.

Example 1.   Solve the equation $|2w + 5| = 8$.

Solution: $2w + 5 = 8$ or $2w + 5 = -8$

$2w = 3$ $2w = -13$

$w = 1.5$ $w = -6.5$

Example 2.   Solve the inequality $|3x - 6| - 1 < 8$ and graph the solution on the number line.

Solution: First isolate the absolute value.

$$|3x - 6| - 1 < 8$$

$$|3x - 6| < 9$$

$$-9 < 3x - 6 < 9$$

$$-3 < 3x < 15$$

$$-1 < x < 5$$

Graph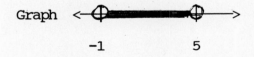

-1   5

Example 3.   Solve the inequality $|5x - 9| \geq 6$ and graph the solution on a number line.

Solution: $|5x - 9| \geq 6$

$5x - 9 \leq -6$ or $5x - 9 \geq 6$

$5x \leq 3$ $5x \geq 15$

$x \leq \dfrac{3}{5}$ $x \geq 3$

Graph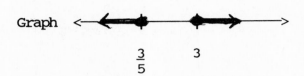

$\dfrac{3}{5}$ 3

Exercise Set 2.6

Solve the equation.

1.) $|2x| = 12$

2.) $|3x - 7| = 5$

3.) $|7x - 2| = 12$

4.) $|3x - 5| + 2 = 7$

Solve the inequality and graph the solution on a number line.

5.) $|4x - 2| < 6$

6.) $|2x + 5| \leq 12$

7.) $|x + 7| + 3 < 9$

8.) $|x - 6| - 5 > 9$

9.) $|2x - 6| \geq 3$

10.) $|2 - 3x| > 4$

-50-

Solution Set for Exercise Set 2.6

1.) {-6, 6}

2.) {2/3, 4}

3.) {-10/7, 2}

4.) {0, 10/3}

5.) -1 < x < 2

6.) -8.5 ≤ x ≤ 3.5

7.) -13 < x < -1

8.) x < -8 or x > 20

9.) x ≤ 1.5 or x ≥ 4.5

10.) x > 2 or x < -2/3

Practice Test

1.) State the degree of $-8xy^2z$.

2.) Solve the equation $5x - 9 = 54$.

3.) Solve the equation $3(2x + 4) = 5(x - 1)$.

4.) Solve the equation $12 - 3(x + 2) = 5(x - 6)$.

5.) The sum of two numbers is 53. One number is two more than twice the other. Find the numbers.

6.) Water is pumped from a well at the rate of 7.5 gallons per minute. How long will it take to pump 135 gallons of water from the well?

7.) Two automobiles start at the same point at the same time and travel in the same direction. One automobile travels at 47 m.p.h. and the other travels at 53 m.p.h. How far apart will they be in 2 1/3 hours?

8.) Mrs. Huard has $18,000 to invest for one year at 6.25% and 8.5%. How much should she invest at each rate if she wishes to earn a total return of $1282.50 on her investment?

9.) How many liters of 8% saline solution must be added to 10 liters of 20% saline solution to get an 18% saline solution?

10.) Solve for y: $15x - 3y = 6$

11.) Solve for ϕ: $S = r\phi$

12.) Solve for x_1: $A = 2Lx_1 + 2x_1h + 2Lh$

Solve the following inequalities.

13.) $3x + 5 < 23$

14.) $4(x + 5) \leq 3(2x - 8)$

15.) $40 - 8x > 3(6x - 2)$

16.) $3 \leq 2x - 9 < 7$

17.) $3x - 5 > 7$ and $x - 2 < 11$

18.) $|x| = 13$

19.) $|x - 9| > 5$

20.) $|2x - 3| \leq 13$

Solution to Practice Test

1.) Fourth

2.) 12.6

3.) x = -17

4.) x = 4.5

5.) 17, 36

6.) 18 minutes

7.) 14 miles

8.) $11,000 at 6.25% and $7,000 at 8.5%

9.) x = 2

10.) y = 5x - 2

11.) $\phi = S/r$

12.) $x_1 = (A - 2Lh)/(2L + 2h)$

13.) x < 6

14.) x ≥ 22

15.) x < 23/13

16.) 6 ≤ x < 8

17.) 4 < x < 13

18.) {-13, 13}

19.) x < 4 or x > 14

20.) -5 ≤ x ≤ 8

Chapter 3   Graphing Linear Equations

Section 3.1   The Cartesian coordinate system, distance and
                midpoint formulas.

Summary:

_____

The Cartesian coordinate system of two axes (or number
lines) in a plane drawn perpendicular to each other. The
horizontal axis is the x axis and the vertical axis is the
y axis. An ordered pair is used to give the two coordinates
of a point. The x coordinate is always the first coordinate
listed in the ordered pair.

_____

Example 1.   Plot each of the following points on the same
               set of axes.

               a.)   A(3, 5)
               b.)   B(-2, 4)
               c.)   C(4, -3)
               d.)   D(-2, -1)

Solution:

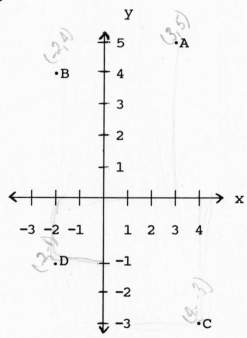

Summary:

The distance, d, between any two points (x_1, y_1) and (x_2, y_2) can be found by the distance formula.

$$d = \sqrt{(x_2 - x_1)^2 + (y_2 - y_1)^2}$$

Example 2.   Determine the distance between the points (2, 5) and (7, 17).

Solution: Let (x_1, y_1) = (2, 5) and (x_2, y_2) = (7, 17) then:

$$d = \sqrt{(x_2 - x_1)^2 + (y_2 - y_1)^2}$$

$$d = \sqrt{(7 - 2)^2 + (17 - 5)^2}$$

$$d = \sqrt{5^2 + 12^2}$$

$$d = \sqrt{25 + 144}$$

$$d = \sqrt{169}$$

$$d = 13$$

Summary:

Given any two points (x_1, y_1) and (x_2, y_2) the point halfway between the given points can be found by the midpoint formula:

$$midpoint = \left(\frac{x_1 + x_2}{2} , \frac{y_1 + y_2}{2} \right)$$

Example 3.   Determine the midpoint of the line segment
              between the points (4, 7) and (−5, 3).

Solution: Let (x_1, y_1) = (4, 7) and (x_2, y_2) = (−5, 3)
              then

$$\text{midpoint} = \left(\frac{x_1 + x_2}{2} \quad , \quad \frac{y_1 + y_2}{2} \right)$$

$$= \left(\frac{4 + (-5)}{2} \quad , \quad \frac{7 + 3}{2} \right)$$

$$= (-1/2, \ 5)$$

Exercise Set 3.1

Plot the following points on the same set of axes.

1.)   a.)   A (4, −2)
      b.)   B (−2, 0)
      c.)   C (−3, 4)
      d.)   D (2, 2)

Plot the following points on the same set of axes.

2.)   a.)   A (4, 7)
      b.)   B (−3, −4)
      c.)   C (−5, 2)
      d.)   D (2, 3)

Determine the distance between the points.

3.)   (4, 7)   and   (1, 3)

4.)   (−5, 2)   and   (2, −3)

5.)   (−2, −1)   and   (−5, −4)

6.)   (2, 4)   and   (8, −5)

−56−

Determine the midpoint of the live segment between the points.

7.) (3, 7) and (9, 11)

8.) (4, 2) and (-2, -8)

9.) (3, 12) and (3, -8)

10.) (0, 5) and (8, 6)

Solution to Exercise Set 3.1

1.)

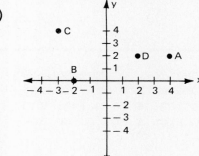

2.)

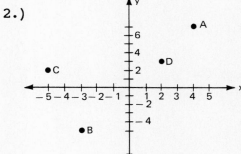

3.) 5

4.) $\sqrt{74}$

5.) $\sqrt{18}$, or $3\sqrt{2}$

6.) $\sqrt{117}$

7.) (6, 9)

8.) (1, -3)

9.) (0, 2)

10.) (4, 5.5)

Section 3.2 Graphing Linear Equations

Summary:

Standard Form of a Linear Equation

$$ax + by = c$$

where **a**, **b**, and **c** are real numbers,
and **a** and **b** are not both zero.

Note:

A graph of an equation is an illustration of the set of
points that satisfy the equation. One method of finding
ordered pairs that satisfy an equation is to solve the
equation for **y**. Then substitute values for **x** and calculate
the corresponding values for **y**.

Example 1. Graph the equation $-4x + 2y = 2$.

Solution: First solve the equation for **y**.

$$-4x + 2y = 2$$

$$2y = 4x + 2$$

$$y = \frac{4x + 2}{2}$$

$$y = 2x + 1$$

Next select three values for **x** and calculate the
corresponding values for **y**.

x value	y value	x	y
$x = 0$	$y = 2(0) + 1 = 1$	0	1
$x = 2$	$y = 2(2) + 1 = 5$	2	5
$x = 3$	$y = 2(3) + 1 = 7$	3	7

-58-

Plot the points and draw the graph.

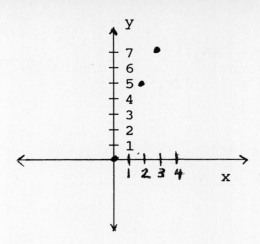

Summary:

x and y intercepts

To find the y intercept, set x = 0 and solve for y.

To find the x intercept, set y = 0 and solve for x.

Note:

The graph of any equation of the form y = a will always be a horizontal line for any real number a.

The graph of any equation of the form x = a will always be a ertical line for any real number a.

Example 2.   Graph the equation 3x + 6y = 12 by plotting the x
and y intercepts.

Solution: To find the y intercept let x = 0 and solve for
y.

$$3x + 6y = 12$$

$$3(0) + 6y = 12$$

$$0 + 6y = 12$$

$$6y = 12$$

$$y = 12$$

The graph crosses the y axis at 2.

To find the x intercept let y = 0 and solve for
x.

$$3x + 6y = 12$$

$$3x + + 6(0) = 12$$

$$3x + 0 = 12$$

$$3x = 12$$

$$x = 4$$

The graph crosses the x axis at 4.

Example 3.   John Rugani was sent three entry blanks for the Genesee River Canoe Race. John intends to make copies of the entry form on a copier machine that produces 38 copies per minute. If Y represents the number of entry forms John has at any minute (M) after John starts copying the entry form, we get the formula Y = 38M + 3.

a.) Draw a graph of minutes versus copies of the entry form that John has after starting the copying machine.

b.) When does John have 98 copies of the entry form?

Solution: Arbitrary select 3 values for M and find the corresponding values for y.

M	Y
0	3
1	41
2	79

Plot the points on a graph.

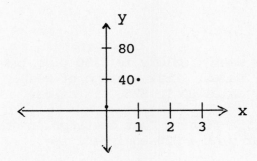

b.) To find when John has 98 copies of the entry form set y = 98 and solve for M.

$$y = 38M + 3$$

$$98 = 38M + 3$$

$$95 = 38M$$

$$2.5 = M$$

Exercise Set 3.2

Graph each equation by solving the equation for **y** and graphing three points on the line.

1.) $2x + y = 4$

2.) $3x + 2y = 8$

3.) $-4x + 2y = 6$

4.) $-2x + 2y = 4$

Graph each equation using **x** and **y** intercepts.

5.) $y = 3x + 4$

6.) $y = -2x + 6$

7.) $2x - 3y = 6$

8.) $-4x + 8y = 4$

9.) Frank Smith's weekly salary is $150 plus 12% commission on his weekly sales. Draw a graph of weekly salary versus weekly sales up to $2500 in sales.

10.) Frank Mandery, a fishing boat operator, rents his boat at $5 per hour plus a $20 equipment fee.

a.) Draw a graph of cost versus hours to rent Mandery's boat and equipment for up to 10 hours.

b.) How long can Angel rent Mandery's boat and equipment if he has $37.50?

Solution to Exercise Set 3.2

1.)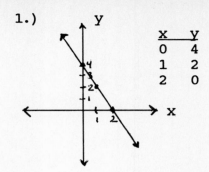

X	Y
0	4
1	2
2	0

2.)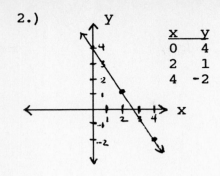

X	Y
0	4
2	1
4	-2

3.)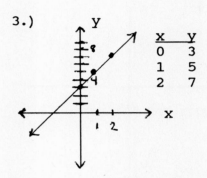

X	Y
0	3
1	5
2	7

4.)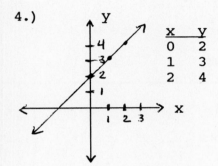

X	Y
0	2
1	3
2	4

5.)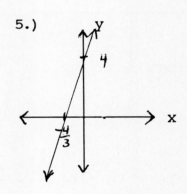

6.)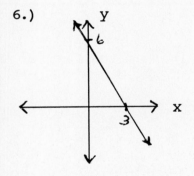

7.)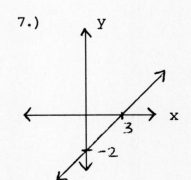

8.)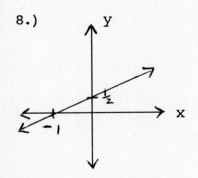

-63-

9.)   Salary

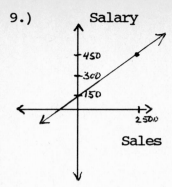

Sales

10a.)   Cost

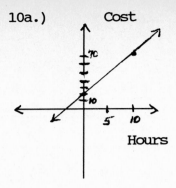

Hours

10b.)   3.5 hours

Section 3.3   Slope of a Line

Summary:

If $x_1 \neq x_2$, the slope of the line through the distinct points (x_1, y_1) and (x_2, y_2) is

$$\text{slope}(M) = \frac{y_2 - y_1}{x_2 - x_1}$$

Example 1.   Find the slope of the line through the points (5, 4) and (3, -1).

Solution: $m = \dfrac{y_2 - y_1}{x_2 - x_1}$

Let $(x_1, y_1) = (5, 4)$ and $(x_2, y_2) = (3, -1)$.

$m = \dfrac{-1 - 4}{3 - 5}$

$m = \dfrac{-5}{-2}$

$m = \dfrac{5}{2}$

Summary:

If line L_1 has slope m_1 and line L_2 has slope m_2, and if $m_1 = m_2$ then lines L_1 and L_2 must be parallel lines.

If line L_1 has slope m_1 and line L_2 has slope m_2, and if $m_1 m_2 = -1$, then L_1 and L_2 must be perpendicular lines.

Example 2.   Two points on L_1 and two points on L_2 are given. Determine if L_1 is parallel to L_2, L_1 is perpendicular to L_2, or neither.

a.) L_1: (0, 2) and (3, 8); L_2: (2, 7) and (5, 13).

b.) L_1: (0, 3) and (1, 8); L_2: (3, 5) and (4, 6).

c.) L_1: (2, 5) and (3, 7); L_2: (4, 6) and (6, 5).

Solution: a.)   Find the slope of L_1.

$$m_1 = \frac{8 - 2}{3 - 0} = \frac{6}{3} = 2$$

Now find the slope of L_2.

$$m_2 = \frac{13 - 7}{5 - 2} = \frac{6}{3} = 2$$

Since $m_1 = m_2$, L_1 and L_2 are parallel.

b.) Find the slope of L_1.

$$m_1 = \frac{8 - 3}{1 - 0} = \frac{5}{1} = 5$$

Find the slope of L_2.

$$m_2 = \frac{6 - 5}{4 - 3} = \frac{1}{1} = 1$$

Since $m_1 \neq m_2$ and $m_1 m_2 \neq -1$, L_1 and L_2 are neither parallel nor perpendicular.

c.) Find the slope of L_1.

$$m_1 = \frac{7 - 5}{3 - 2} = \frac{2}{1} = 2$$

Find the slope of L_2.

$$m_2 = \frac{5 - 6}{6 - 4} = \frac{-1}{2}$$

Since $m_1 m_2 = 2 \cdot (-\tfrac{1}{2}) = -1$, the lines L_1 and L_2 are perpendicular.

Exercise Set 3.3

Find the slope of the line through the given points.

1.) (3, 5) and (7, 8)

2.) (-4, 2) and (-3, 8)

3.) (5, -7) and (-8, 2)

4.) (-5, -11) and (4, -3)

To points on L_1 and two points on L_2 are given. Determine if L_1 is parallel to L_2, L_1 is perpendicular to L_2, or neither.

5.) L_1: (3, 5) and (4, 7); L_2: (8, 7) and (10, 6).

6.) L_1: (-3, 2) and (-4, -3); L_2: (4, 7) and (5, 11).

7.) L_1: (7, 10) and (11, 13); L_2: (8, 11) and (12, 14).

8.) L_1: (9, -5) and (4, 6); L_2: (3, -2) and (-2, -5).

Solution to Exercise Set 3.3

1.) $\dfrac{3}{4}$ 2.) 6   3.) $\dfrac{-9}{13}$ 4.) $\dfrac{8}{9}$

5.) Perpendicular   6.) Neither

7.) Parallel   8.) Neither

Section 3.4 Slope-Intercept and Point-Slope Forms of a Line.

Summary:

Slope-Intercept Form of a Line

$$y = mx + b$$

where **m** is the **slope** and **b** is the **y intercept** of the line.

Example 1. Write the equation $-2x + 8y = 3$ in slope intercept form. State the slope and the **y** intercept.

Solution: To write an equation in slope intercept form,
             solve it for **y**.

$$-2x + 8y = 3$$

$$8y = 2x + 3$$

$$y = \frac{2x + 3}{8}$$

$$y = \frac{1}{4}x + \frac{3}{8}$$

The slope is $\frac{1}{4}$ and the y intercept is $\frac{3}{8}$.

Example 2.   Determine if the following lines are parallel,
              perpendicular or neither.

$$2x + 4y = 8$$

$$3x + 6y = 2$$

Solution: Recall two lines with slopes m_1 and m_2 are

             parallel if $m_1 = m_2$ and are perpendicular if

             $m_1 m_2 = -1$.

$2x + 4y = 8$ $\qquad\qquad$ $3x + 6y = 2$

$\quad 4y = -2x + 8$ $\qquad\qquad$ $\quad 6y = -3x + 2$

$\quad y = -\frac{1}{2}x + 2$ $\qquad\qquad$ $\quad y = -\frac{1}{2}x + \frac{1}{3}$

Since $m_1 = m_2 = -\frac{1}{2}$, the lines are perpendicular.

Summary:

_____

Point-Slope Form of a Line

$$y - y_1 = m(x - x_1)$$

where **m** is the slope of the line and the point $(x_1 y_1)$ is a

point on the line.

_____

Example 3. Write an equation of the line through the point
(-3, 5) with a slope of 3.

Solution: Let $m = 3$ and $(x_1, y_1) = (-3, 5)$.

Use the point-slope form of a line.

$$y - y_1 = m(x - x_1)$$

$$y - 5 = 3[x - (-3)]$$

$$y - 5 = 3(x + 3)$$

$$y - 5 = 3x + 9$$

$$y = 3x + 14$$

Example 4. Determine, in slope-intercept form, the equation
of the line parallel to the line $2y = -4x + 8$ and
passes through the point (3, 5).

Solution: First find the slope of the given line.

$$2y = -4x + 8$$

$$y = -2x + 4$$

The slope is -2.

Now find the equation of a line with slope -2 and passing through the point (3, 5).

$$y - y_1 = m(x - x_1)$$

$$y - 5 = -2(x - 3)$$

$$y - 5 = -2x + 6$$

$$y = -2x + 11$$

Exercise Set 3.4

Write the following equations in slope-intercept form.

1.) $3x + 6y = -9$ 2.) $5x + 2y = 9$

Write the equation of the line with the given slope and passing through the given point.

3.) $m = 3$; (5, 2)   4.) $m = -2$; (-1, 3)

5.) $m = \dfrac{3}{4}$; (-2, 2)

Determine if the two given lines are parallel, perpendicular or neither.

6.) $y = -2x - 4$ 7.) $3y = 6x + 5$

   $y = \dfrac{1}{2}x + 8$ $-2y = -4x - 9$

8.) $3x + 4y = 5$

   $-9x + 8y = 12$

Find the equation of a line with the properties given. Write the equation in slope-intercept form.

9.) Through (6, 7) and parallel to $2x - 3y = 8$.

10.) Through (-2, 4) and perpendicular to $3x + y = 2$.

Solution to Exercise Set 3.4

1.) $y = -\dfrac{1}{2}x - \dfrac{3}{2}$ 2.) $y = -\dfrac{5}{2}x + \dfrac{9}{2}$

3.) $y = 3x - 13$ 4.) $y = -2x + 1$

5.) $y = \dfrac{3}{4}x + \dfrac{7}{2}$ 6.) Perpendicular

7.) Parallel   8.) Neither

9.) $y = \dfrac{2}{3}x + 3$ 10.) $y = \dfrac{1}{3}x + \dfrac{14}{3}$

Section 3.5 Relations and Functions

Summary:

A **relation** is any set of ordered pairs.

The **domain** of a relationship is the set of
   first coordinates in the set of ordered pairs.

The **range** of a relation is the set of
   second coordinates in the set of ordered pairs.

Example 1. State the domain and range of each relation.

a.) $\{(1, 3), (2, 5), (7, 9), (2, 1), (4, 6)\}$

b.)

x	1	3	5	7
y	2	4	6	8

c.) $y = 2x + 3$, for $1 \leq x \leq 3$, $x \in N$.

-71-

Solution: a.) Domain {1, 2, 4, 7}
             Range {1, 3, 5, 6, 9}

           b.) Domain {1, 3, 5, 7}
             Range {2, 4, 6, 8}

           c.) Use y = 2x + 3 to form a table
                for x = 1, 2, or 3.

x	1	2	3
y	5	7	9

                Domain {1, 2, 3}
                Range {5, 7, 9}

Summary:

A **function** is a set of distinct ordered pairs in which no
two ordered pairs have the same first coordinate. If a
vertical line cannot be drawn to intersect the graph at
more than one point, then the graph is a graph of a
function.

Example 2. Determine whether the following relations are
            functions.

            a.) {(1, 3), (2, 5), (7, 9), (2, 1), (4, 6)}

            b.) | x | 1 | 3 | 5 | 7 |
                 |---|---|---|---|---|
                 | y | 2 | 4 | 6 | 8 |

            c.)

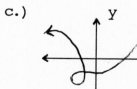

Solution: a.)   Not a function because the ordered pairs
                  (2, 5) and (2, 1) have the same first
                  coordinate.

            b.)   A function.

            c.)   Not a function. We can find a vertical line
                  that intersects the graph at more than one
                  point.

Summary:

The notation $y = f(x)$ is used to show that **y** is a function
of the variable **x**.

For example, $y = 2x + 3$ can be written as $f(x) = 2x + 3$.
If we want to find the value of the function at $x = 5$, we
write $f(5) = 2(5) + 3 = 13$.

Example 3.   For $f(x) = 3x - 1$, find:

             a.) $f(2)$

             b.) $f(-4)$

Solution: a.) $f(x) = 3x - 1$

                   $f(2) = 3(2) - 1$

                   $f(2) = 6 - 1$

                   $f(2) = 5$

             b.) $f(x) = 3x - 1$

                   $f(-4) = 3(-4) - 1$

                   $f(-4) = -12 - 1$

                   $f(-4) = -13$

Exercise Set 3.5

Determine which of the relations are also functions.
Give the range and domain of each relation or function.

1.) {(0, 1), (1, 3), (2, 5), (3, 6), (4, 9)}

2.)
x	-2	-2	0	1	2
y	5	4	3	4	1

3.) {(0, 2), (2, 3), (3, 4), (3, 5), (4, 7)}

4.) y = 3x - 2, for 1 ≤ x ≤ 5, x ∈ N.

5.)

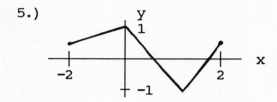

Evaluate the functions at the values indicated.

6.) f(x) = 2x - 5   find   a.) f(3)   b.) f(7)

7.) f(x) = -2x + 1   find   a.) f(-2)   b.) f(0)

8.) f(x) = .5x + 2   find   a.) f(-2)   b.) f(4)

Solution to Exercise Set 3.5

1.) Function,
      Domain {0, 1, 2, 3, 4}, Range {1, 3, 5, 6, 9}

2.) Not a function,
      Domain {-2, -1, 0, 1, 2}, Range {1, 3, 4, 5}

3.) Not a function,
      Domain {0, 2, 3, 4}, Range {2, 3, 4, 5, 7}

4.) Function,
     Domain {1, 2, 3, 4, 5}, Range {1, 4, 7, 10, 13}

5.) Function,
     Domain {x|−2 ≤ x ≤ 2}, Range {y|−1 ≤ y ≤ 1}

6.) a.) 1   b.) 9

7.) a.) 5   b.) 1

8.) a.) 1   b.) 4

Section 3.6 Graphing Linear Inequalities

Summary:

To Graph a Linear Inequality

1. Replace the inequality with an equal sign.

2. Draw the graph of the equation in step 1. If the
   original inequality contained a ≥ or ≤ symbol, draw
   the graph using a solid line. Otherwise, use a dashed
   line to draw the graph.

3. Select any point not on the line and determine if this
   point is a solution to the original inequality. If the
   point selected is a solution, shade the region on the
   side of the line containing this point. If the point
   selected does not satisfy the equation, shade the region
   on the side of the line not containing the point.

Example 1.   Graph the inequality y < 2x - 1.

Solution: Graph the line y = 2x - 1 but since the original
             inequality is < use a dashed line.

             Next, select a point not on the line, such as
             (2, 0).

             See if (2, 0) satisfies the inequality.

             y < 2x - 1

             0 < 2(2) - 1

             0 < 3   True

             Since the point (2, 0) satisfies the inequality,
             shade the region on the side of the line
             containing (2, 0).

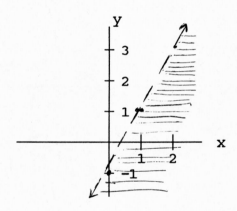

Exercise Set 3.6

Graph each inequality.

  1.) y > x + 1

  2.) y ≥ -x + 1

  3.) y < 3x

  4.) y ≤ 2x + 2

Solution to Exercise Set 3.6

1.)

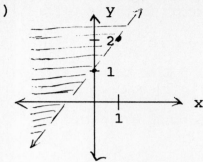

2.)

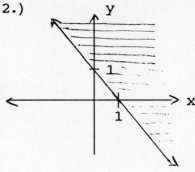

3.)

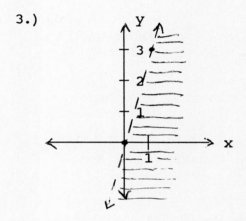

2.)

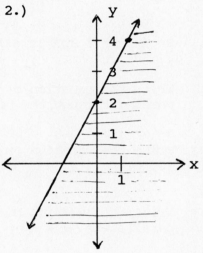

Practice Test

1.) Draw the ordered pairs on the same set of axes.

    a.) A(3, 2)   b.) B(-2, 5)

    c.) C(0, -2)   d.) D(-3, -4)

2.) Find the distance between the points (3, 5) and (4,-6).

3.) Find the midpoint of the line segment between the
    points (-3, -5) and (18, -2).

4.) Graph the equation $-3x + 2y = 8$.

5.) Determine the slope and y intercept of the equation $18x + 6y = 12$.

6.) Find the value for the slope of a line through the points $(-2, 5)$ and $(-4, -7)$.

Two points on L_1 and two points on L_2 are parallel, perpendicular, or neither.

7.) $y = 2x + 4$ and $8y = 16x - 2$.

8.) $-3x + 2y = -3$ and $4x + 6y = 2$.

9.) $8x + 5y = 7$ and $3x - 7y = 12$.

10.) Write the equation of a line with slope $= -3$ and passing through the point $(1, 5)$.

11.) Write the equation of the line through $(4, 0)$ and $(0, 2)$.

12.) Write the equation of the line through $(4, 2)$ that is parallel to $-x + 2y = 2$.

13.) Write the equation of the line through $(-1, -3)$ and perpendicular to the line $y = 3x - 2$.

14.) Write the domain and range for the relation $\{(1, 5), (2, 10), (3, 15), (4, 20)\}$.

15.) Determine if $3x + 6y = 12$ is a function for $2 \le x \le 5$ and $x \in N$.

Write the domain and range for this relation.

Graph the following equations and inequalities.

16.) $y \leq x + 4$

17.) $y > 2x - 2$

18.) $y < x - 3$

19.) $y \geq 3x - 1$

20.) $y \leq -3x + 4$

Solution to Practice Test

1.)

2.) $\sqrt{122}$

3.) $(7.5, -3.5)$

4.)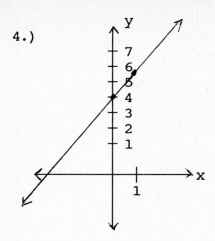

5.) Slope = -3
    y intercept = 2

6.) Slope = 6

7.) Parallel

8.) Perpendicular

9.) Neither

10.) $y = -3x + 8$

11.) $y = -\frac{1}{2}x + 2$

12.) $y = \frac{1}{2}x$

13.) $y = -\frac{1}{3}x - \frac{10}{3}$

14.) Domain {1, 2, 3, 4}; Range {5, 10, 15, 20}

15.) Function,
     Domain {2, 3, 4, 5}; Range {1, $\frac{1}{2}$, 0, $-\frac{1}{2}$}

16.)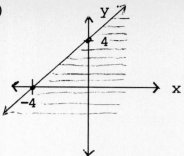

17.)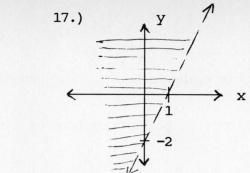

18.)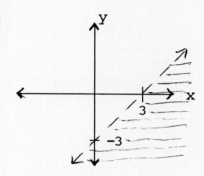

19.)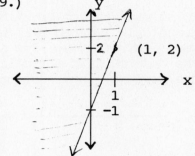

20.)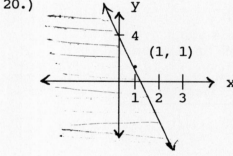

Chapter 4   Systems of Linear Equations and Inequalities

Section 4.1   Solving Systems of Linear Equations

Summary:

To solve a system of linear equations in two variables graphically, graph all equations in the system on the same set of axes. The solution to the system will be the ordered pair (or pairs) common to all the lines, or the point of intersection of all lines in the system.

Note:

A **consistent** system of equations has exactly one solution.   An **inconsistent** system of equations has no solution.

Example 1.   Solve the following system of equations graphically.

$$y = 2x + 5$$

$$y = x + 9$$

$$y = 2x + 5$$
$$2x - 5 = 2 \div -5$$
$$y = x + 9 - 9 =$$
$$y = 0$$
$$y = 3$$

Solution: Graph both equations on the same set of axes.

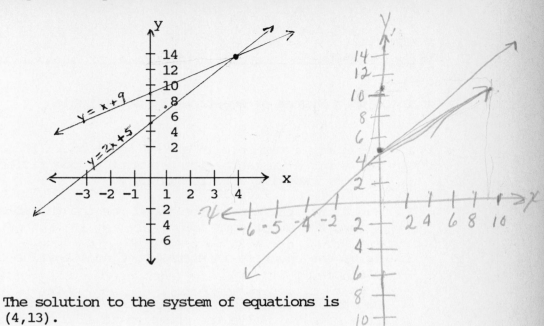

The solution to the system of equations is (4,13).

Example 2. Determine if the ordered pair (2, 5) satisfies the system of linear equations.

$$y = x + 3$$

$$y = 2x + 1$$

Solution: Substitute $x = 2$ and $y = 5$ into both equations to determine if the ordered pair (2, 5) is on both lines.

$y = x + 3$	$y = 2x + 1$
$5 = 2 + 3$	$5 = 2(2) + 1$
$5 = 5$	$5 = 5$

The ordered pair (2, 5) is on both lines. Therefore, (2, 5) satisfies the system of linear equations.

Summary:

_____

To Solve a System of Equations by Substitution

1. Solve for a variable in either equation. (If possible solve for a variable with a numerical coefficient of 1 to avoid working with fractions.)

2. Substitute the expression found for the variable in step 1 into the other equation.

3. Solve the equation in step 2 to find the value of one variable.

4. Substitute the value found in step 3 into the equation from step 1. Solve the equation to find the remaining variable.

_____

Example 3.   Solve the following system of equations by substitution.

$$2x + 3y = 8$$

$$x + 4y = 2$$

Solution: Solve $x + 4y = 2$ for x.

$$x + 4y = 2$$

$$x = -4y + 2$$

-84-

Substitute $x = -4y + 2$ for x in the equation $2x + 3y = 8$, and solve for y.

$$2x + 3y = 8$$

$$2(-4y + 2) + 3y = 8$$

$$-8y + 4 + 3y = 8$$

$$-5y + 4 = 8$$

$$-5y = 4$$

$$y = -\frac{4}{5}$$

Substitute $y = -\frac{4}{5}$ into $x = -4y + 2$,

and solve for x.

$$x = -4y + 2$$

$$x = -4 - \frac{4}{5} + 2$$

$$x = \frac{16}{5} + \frac{10}{5}$$

$$x = \frac{26}{5}$$

$$x = 5\frac{1}{5}$$

Summary:

To Solve a System of Equations by the Addition Method

1. If necessary, rewrite each equation so that terms containing variables appear on the left side of the equal sign and any constants appear on the right side of the equal sign.

2. If necessary, multiply one or both equations by a constant(s) so that when the equations are added, the resulting sum will contain only one variable.

3. Add the respective sides of the equations. This will result in a single equation in only one variable.

4. Solve for the variable in the equation in step 3.

5. Substitute the value found in step 4 into either of the original equations and solve for the value of the remaining variable.

Example 4. Solve the following system of linear equations by the addition method.

$$2x = 5y + 9$$

$$3x + 10y = 2$$

Solution: Rearrange the first equation to have the variable on the left hand side of the equation.

$$2x - 5y = 6$$

$$3x + 10y = 2$$

Multiply both sides of the first equation by 2.

$$2(2x - 5y) = 2(6) \quad \text{gives} \quad 4x - 10y = 12$$

$$3x + 10y = 2 \qquad\qquad\qquad 3x + 10y = 2$$

Add the respective sides of the two equations to get

$$7x = 14 \quad \text{or} \quad x = 2.$$

Substitute $x = 2$ into $3x + 10y = 2$, and solve for y.

$$3x + 10y = 2$$

$$3(2) + 10y = 2$$

$$6 + 10y = 2$$

$$10y = -4$$

$$y = -.4$$

Exercise Set 4.1

Solve the following system of equations graphically.

1.) $y = 3x + 1$ 2.) $y = 4x - 5$

     $y = 2x + 4$ $y = 5x - 6$

Determine if the ordered pair satisfies the system of linear equations.

3.) $(2, -3)$; $y = 3x - 9$ and $y = 4x - 11$

4.) $(3, 2)$; $y = 3x - 7$ and $y = x + 1$

Solve the system of linear equations by the substitution method.

5.) $y = 2x + 5$ 6.) $2y = x - 10$

     $2x + 3y = 8$ $y + 10 = 3x$

7.) $4y = 2x - 1$

     $2y = 4x + 2$

Solve the system of linear equations by the addition method.

8.) $2x - 3y = 8$ 9.) $2x = 2y + 1$

$2x + 3y = -4$ $4x + y = 7$

10.) $3x - 4y = 7$

$2x - 3y = 4$

Solution to Exercise Set 4.1

1.) $(3, 10)$ 2.) $(1, -1)$ 3.) True

4.) False $(2 \neq 3 + 1)$

5.) $\left(\frac{3}{8}, 5\frac{3}{4}\right)$ 6.) $(2, -4)$ 7.) $\left(\frac{-5}{6}, -\frac{2}{3}\right)$

8.) $(1, -2)$ 9.) $\left(\frac{3}{2}, 1\right)$ 10.) $(5, 2)$

Section 4.2 Third-Ordered Systems of Linear Equations

Summary:

A third-order system consists of three equations with three unknowns. Examples of how to solve third-order systems of linear equations by the substitution and the addition method will be described without formally stating the procedures.

Example 1. Solve the system of equations given below by substitution.

$$x = 5$$

$$2x + 3y = 4$$

$$4x - 5y - 2z = 10$$

Solution: Substitute x = 5 into 2x + 3y = 4 and solve for y.

$$2x + 3y = 4$$

$$2(5) + 3y = 4$$

$$10 + 3y = 4$$

$$3y = -6$$

$$y = -2$$

Now substitute x = 5 and y = -2 into the third equation and solve for z.

$$4x - 5y - 2z = 10$$

$$4(5) - 5(-2) - 2z = 10$$

$$20 + 10 - 2z = 10$$

$$30 - 2z = 10$$

$$-2z = -20$$

$$z = 10$$

The solution is (x, y, z) = (5, -2, 10).

Example 2. Solve the system of equations by the addition method.

$$4x + 2y + 7z = -10 \qquad \text{(equation a)}$$

$$3x - 4y - 2z = 29 \qquad \text{(equation b)}$$

$$-2x + 5y + 4z = -34 \qquad \text{(equation c)}$$

Solution: Use equation b and c to eliminate the variable z.
              Multiply each side of equation b by 2.

$$2(3x - 4y - 2z) = (29)2 \text{ gives } 6x - 8y - 4z = 58$$

and add equation c. $\underline{-2x + 5y + 4z = -34}$

The resulting equation d is: $4x - 3y \qquad = 24$

If we multiply both sides of equation a by 2 and
multiply both sides of equation b by 7   and add
the resulting equation, we will again eliminate
the z variable.

$$2(4x + 2y + 7z) = (-10)2 \text{ gives } 8x + 4y + 14z = -20$$

$$7(3x - 4y - 2z) = (29)7 \text{ gives } \underline{21x - 28y - 14z = 203}$$

The resulting equation e is: $29x - 24y \qquad = 183.$

We now have equations d and e in two variables
and can solve for the variables by the addition
method used in the previous section.

$$(8)(4x - 3y) \qquad = (24)(8) \text{ gives } 32x - 24y = 192$$

$$(-1)(29x - 24y) = (183)(-1) \qquad \underline{-29x + 24y = -183}$$

$$3x \qquad = 9$$

$$x \qquad = 3$$

Substituting x = 3 into 4x - 3y = 24

$$4(3) - 3y = 24$$

$$12 - 3y = 24$$

$$-3y = 12$$

$$y = -4$$

Substituting x = 3 and y = -4 into

$$4x + 2y + 7z = -10$$

$$4(3) + 2(-4) + 7z = -10$$

$$12 + (-8) + 7z = -10$$

$$4 + 7z = -10$$

$$7z = -14$$

$$z = -2$$

Note:

The process of solving a system of third-order equations, requires that the third-ordered system in three variables be changed by the addition method to a system of two equations in two variables. Then final solution of the system of equations is possible. Which variable to eliminate in moving from a third-ordered system to a second-order system is your choice.

Exercise Set 4.2

Solve by the substitution method.

1.) $x = 3$

$x + 2y = 7$

$-2x + y + z = 2$

2.) $2x + 3y = 5$

$y = 1$

$2y + 3z = 11$

3.) $3x = -12$

$3x + 2y = 8$

$x + y - z = 14$

Solve by using the addition method.

4.) $5x + 6y - 4z = -8$

$2x + 4y + 5z = 15$

$-8x - 4y + 5z = 3$

5.) $x + y + z = 9$

$2x - 3y + 4z = 11$

$3x - 2y - 2z = -8$

6.) $3x - 2y + 4z = -8$

$5x + 6y + 4z = -16$

$x + 3y - 2z = 10$

Solution to Exercise Set 4.2

1.) $x = 3$ 2.) $x = 1$ 3.) $x = -4$

$y = 2$ $y = 1$ $y = 10$

$z = 6$ $z = 3$ $z = 8$

4.) $x = 2$ 5.) $x = 2$ 6.) $x = 4$

$y = -1$ $y = 3$ $y = -2$

$z = 3$ $z = 4$ $z = -6$

Section 4.3 Applications of System Linear Equations

Example 1. Ray Smith bicycles to school with the wind at 6.5 m.p.h. and back home from school against the wind at 4.75 m.p.h. What is Ray's speed of bicycling unaided by the wind?

Solution: Let x = the speed in m.p.h. that Ray bicycles if there were no wind

Let y = the wind speed

$$x + y = 6.5 \text{ m.p.h.}$$

$$x - y = 4.75 \text{ m.p.h.}$$

$$2x = 11.25$$

$$x = 5.625 \text{ m.p.h.}$$

Example 2. A canoeist takes 4 hours to paddle to a point upstream and 2 hours to return. If the water current is 2 m.p.h.:

a.) find the speed of the canoeist in still water;

b.) how far did the canoeist travel upstream?

Solution: Let x = the speed of the canoeist in still water

               Let x + 2 = the speed of the canoeist going
                            downstream

               Let x - 2 = the speed of the canoeist going
                            upstream

               Recall: **distance = rate · time**

               Upstream distance = (x - 2)(4) = 4x - 8
               Downstream distance = (x + 2)(2) = 2x + 4

               Since the upstream and downstream distances are
               equal   4x - 8 = 2x + 4

                          2x - 8 =   4

                            2x = 12

                             x =   6

Example 3.   Pat mixes a 20% fruit juice drink with a 75%
fruit juice drink to get 32 liters of a 50% fruit
juice drink.   How many liters of 75% solution
does she mix?

Solution: Let x = the number of liters of 75% fruit juice
                           drink

               Let y = the number of liters of 20% fruit juice
                           drink

                   x + y = 32   Total volume 32 liters.

               .75x + .20y = .5(32)   The percentage of fruit
                                      juice in the drink.

Multiply both sides of the first equation by -.75

$$(-.75)(x + y) = (32)(-.75) \text{ gives } -.75x - .75y = -24$$

$$\underline{.75x + .20y = 16}$$

$$-.55y = -8$$

$$y = 14.54$$

Since **y** is approximately equal to 14.55 liters, substitute this value into x + y = 32 to solve for **x**.

$$x + y = 32$$

$$x + 14.55 = 32$$

$$x = 17.45$$

Exercise Set 4.3

Express the problems as a system of linear equations and solve.

1.) A motorboat can travel 48 m.p.h. with the current and 35 m.p.h. against the current when traveling at top speed. Find the top speed of the motorboat in still water.

2.) Robert bicycles from home to school in 60 minutes against the wind and from school to home in 30 minutes with the wind. If the wind was 6 m.p.h. on this day, what is Robert's bicycling speed on a calm day.

3.) Mr. Mandery can fly from Sodus Point to Bar Harbor in 1 hour and back in 1½ hours. If he has a 10 m.p.h. wind aiding his trip to Bar Harbor and a 10 m.p.h. wind against him in his return to Sodus Point, and his airplane is traveling at its maximum speed, what is the maximum speed of his airplane on a calm day?

4.) Ann has a 30% acid solution and a 50% acid solution. How much of each solution must she mix to get 12.5 liters of 48% acid solution?

5.) Chris Brown has 2% butterfat milk and 5% butterfat milk. How much of each type of milk must she mix to get 120 gallons of 2½% milk?

Solution to Exercise 4.3

1.) 41.5 m.p.h.

2.) 18 m.p.h.

3.) 50 m.p.h.

4.) 1.25 liters of 30% acid solution
11.25 liters of 50% acid solution

5.) 100 gallons of 2% butterfat milk
20 gallons of 5% butterfat milk

Section 4.4 Solving Systems of Equations by Determinants (optional).

Summary:

Value of a Second-Order Determinant

$$\begin{vmatrix} a_1 & b_1 \\ a_2 & b_2 \end{vmatrix} = a_1b_2 - a_2b_1$$

Example 1. Find the value $\begin{vmatrix} 7 & 6 \\ 3 & 8 \end{vmatrix}$

Solution: $\begin{vmatrix} 7 & 6 \\ 3 & 8 \end{vmatrix} = 7(8) - 3(6)$

$= 56 - 18$

$= 38$

Summary:

Cramer's Rule

For a system of equations of the form

$$a_1x + b_1y = c_1$$

$$a_2x + b_2y = c_2$$

$$x = \frac{\begin{vmatrix} c_1 & b_1 \\ c_2 & b_2 \end{vmatrix}}{\begin{vmatrix} a_1 & b_1 \\ a_2 & b_2 \end{vmatrix}} = \frac{D_x}{D} \quad \text{and} \quad y = \frac{\begin{vmatrix} a_1 & c_1 \\ a_2 & c_2 \end{vmatrix}}{\begin{vmatrix} a_1 & b_1 \\ a_2 & b_2 \end{vmatrix}} = \frac{D_y}{D}$$

Example 2.   Use determinants to evaluate the following system.

$$3x - 2y = 7$$

$$8x + 3y = 52$$

Solution: Both equations are of the form ax + by = c.
Therefore,

Let $a_1 = 3$, $b_1 = -2$, $c_1 = 7$

Let $a_2 = 8$, $b_2 = 3$, and $c_2 = 52$

$$D = \begin{vmatrix} a_1 & b_1 \\ a_2 & b_2 \end{vmatrix} = \begin{vmatrix} 3 & -2 \\ 8 & 3 \end{vmatrix} = 3(3) - 8(-2) = 25$$

$$D_x = \begin{vmatrix} c_1 & b_1 \\ c_2 & b_2 \end{vmatrix} = \begin{vmatrix} 7 & -2 \\ 52 & 3 \end{vmatrix} = 7(3) - 52(-2) = 125$$

$$D_y = \begin{vmatrix} a_1 & c_1 \\ a_2 & c_2 \end{vmatrix} = \begin{vmatrix} 3 & 7 \\ 8 & 52 \end{vmatrix} = 3(52) - 8(7) = 100$$

$$x = \frac{D_x}{D} = \frac{125}{25} = 5$$

$$y = \frac{D_x}{D} = \frac{100}{25} = 4$$

Thus, the solution is x = 5, y = 4 or the ordered
pair (5, 4).

Summary:

<u>A third-ordered determinant is evaluated as follows:</u>

$$
\begin{vmatrix} a_1 & b_1 & c_1 \\ a_2 & b_2 & c_2 \\ a_3 & b_3 & c_3 \end{vmatrix} = a_1 \begin{vmatrix} b_2 & c_2 \\ b_3 & c_3 \end{vmatrix} - a_2 \begin{vmatrix} b_1 & c_1 \\ b_3 & c_3 \end{vmatrix} + a_3 \begin{vmatrix} b_1 & c_1 \\ b_2 & c_2 \end{vmatrix}
$$

with the first minor labeled "minor determinant of a_1", the second "minor determinant of a_2", and the third "minor determinant of a_3".

Example 3. Evaluate $\begin{vmatrix} 4 & 2 & 7 \\ 3 & -4 & -2 \\ -2 & 5 & 4 \end{vmatrix}$

Solution: Let $a_1 = 4 \qquad b_1 = 2 \qquad c_1 = 7$

$\qquad\qquad\qquad a_2 = 3 \qquad b_2 = -4 \qquad c_2 = -2$

$\qquad\qquad\qquad a_3 = -2 \qquad b_3 = 5 \qquad c_3 = 4$

$$
\begin{vmatrix} 4 & 2 & 7 \\ 3 & -4 & -2 \\ -2 & 5 & 4 \end{vmatrix} = 4 \begin{vmatrix} -4 & -2 \\ 5 & 4 \end{vmatrix} - (3) \begin{vmatrix} 2 & 7 \\ 5 & 4 \end{vmatrix} + (-2) \begin{vmatrix} 2 & 7 \\ -4 & -2 \end{vmatrix}
$$

$= 4[-4(4) - 5(-2)] - 3[2(4) - 5(7)] - 2[2(-2) - (-4)7]$

$= 4[-16 + 10] - 3[8 - 35] - 2[-4 + 28]$

$= 4(-6) - 3(-27) - 2(24)$

$= -24 + 81 - 48$

$= 9$

The determinant has a value of 9.

Summary:

To evaluate the system

$$a_1x + b_1y + c_1z = d_1$$

$$a_2x + b_2y + c_2z = d_2$$

$$a_3x + b_2y + c_3z = d_3$$

with

$$D = \begin{vmatrix} a_1 & b_1 & c_1 \\ a_2 & b_2 & c_2 \\ a_3 & b_3 & c_3 \end{vmatrix} \qquad D_x = \begin{vmatrix} d_1 & b_1 & c_1 \\ d_2 & b_2 & c_2 \\ d_3 & b_3 & c_3 \end{vmatrix}$$

$$D_y = \begin{vmatrix} a_1 & d_1 & c_1 \\ a_2 & d_2 & c_2 \\ a_3 & d_3 & c_3 \end{vmatrix} \qquad D_x = \begin{vmatrix} a_1 & b_1 & d_1 \\ a_2 & b_2 & d_2 \\ a_3 & b_3 & d_3 \end{vmatrix}$$

then

$$x = \frac{D_x}{D}, \qquad y = \frac{D_y}{D}, \qquad z = \frac{D_z}{D}$$

Example 4. Solve the system of equations using determinants.

$$4x + 2y + 7z = -10$$

$$3x - 4y - 2z = 29$$

$$-2x + 5y + 4z = -34$$

Solution: $a_1 = 4$ $b_1 = 2$ $c_1 = 7$ $d_1 = -10$

$a_2 = 3$ $b_2 = -4$ $c_2 = -2$ $d_2 = 29$

$a_3 = -2$ $b_3 = 5$ $c_3 = 4$ $d_3 = -34$

$$D = \begin{vmatrix} 4 & 2 & 7 \\ 3 & -4 & -2 \\ -2 & 5 & 4 \end{vmatrix} = 4 \begin{vmatrix} -4 & -2 \\ 5 & 4 \end{vmatrix} - 3 \begin{vmatrix} 2 & 7 \\ 5 & 4 \end{vmatrix} + (-2) \begin{vmatrix} 2 & 7 \\ -4 & -2 \end{vmatrix}$$

$$= 4(-6) - 3(-27) - 2(24)$$

$$= -24 + 81 - 48$$

$$= 9$$

$$D_x = \begin{vmatrix} -10 & 2 & 7 \\ 29 & -4 & -2 \\ -34 & 5 & 4 \end{vmatrix} = -10 \begin{vmatrix} -4 & -2 \\ 5 & 4 \end{vmatrix} - 29 \begin{vmatrix} 2 & 7 \\ 5 & 4 \end{vmatrix} + (-34) \begin{vmatrix} 2 & 7 \\ -4 & 2 \end{vmatrix}$$

$$= -10(-6) - 29(-27) - (34)(24)$$

$$= 60 + 783 - 816$$

$$= 27$$

$$D_y = \begin{vmatrix} 4 & -10 & 7 \\ 3 & 29 & -2 \\ -2 & -34 & 4 \end{vmatrix} = 4 \begin{vmatrix} 29 & -2 \\ -34 & 4 \end{vmatrix} - 3 \begin{vmatrix} -10 & 7 \\ -34 & 4 \end{vmatrix} + (-2) \begin{vmatrix} -10 & 7 \\ 29 & -2 \end{vmatrix}$$

$$= 4(48) - 3(198) - 2(-183)$$

$$= 192 - 594 + 366$$

$$= -36$$

$$D_z = \begin{vmatrix} 4 & 2 & -10 \\ 3 & -4 & 29 \\ -2 & 5 & -34 \end{vmatrix} = 4 \begin{vmatrix} -4 & 29 \\ 5 & -34 \end{vmatrix} - 3 \begin{vmatrix} 2 & -10 \\ 5 & -34 \end{vmatrix} + (-2) \begin{vmatrix} 2 & -10 \\ -4 & 29 \end{vmatrix}$$

$$= 4(-9) - 3(-18) - 2(18)$$

$$= -36 + 54 - 36$$

$$= -18$$

$$x = \frac{D_x}{D} = \frac{27}{9} = 3$$

$$y = \frac{D_y}{D} = \frac{-36}{9} = -4$$

$$z = \frac{D_z}{D} = \frac{-18}{9} = -2$$

The solution to the system is (3, -4, -2).

Exercise Set 4.4

Solve the system of equations using determinants.

1.) $4x - 6y = 42$

   $-8x + 2y = -34$

2.) $5x + 6y = -9$

   $4x - 2y = -14$

3.) $6x + 5y = -64$

   $4x + 7y = -72$

4.) $8x - 3y = 5$

   $4x - 6y = 4$

Solve the system of equations using determinants.

5.)　　2x + 3y + 4z =　　1　　　　6.)　　4x + 4y - 10z = 16

　　　　-6x - 3y - 2z =　11　　　　　　　6x + 3y -　8z = 26

　　　　8x - 4y - 6z = -24　　　　　　　-2x - 2y + 6z =　-6

7.)　　3x + 2y - 4z =　-3　　　　8.)　　3x + 4y - 2z = -10

　　　　8x - 6y + 2z =　16　　　　　　　-3x - 6y + 4z =　20

　　　　-2x + 7y - 2z = -11　　　　　　-5x +　y + 2z =　29

Solution to Exercise Set 4.4

1.)　(x, y) = (3, -5)　　　　　　2.)　(x, y) = (-3, 1)

3.)　(x, y) = (-4, -8)　　　　　4.)　(x, y) = (1/2, 1/3)

5.)　(x, y, z) = (-2, -1, 2)　　6.)　(x, y, z) = (5, 4, 2)

7.)　(x, y, z) = (1, -1, 1)　　8.)　(x, y, z) = (-2, 3, 8)

Section 4.5　Solving Systems of Linear Inequalities

Summary:

To Solve a System of Linear Inequalities

Graph each inequality on the same set of axes.　The solution
is the　set of points that satisfies all the inequalities in
the system.

Example 1.   Determine the solution to the system of
             inequalities.

$$2x - y < 8$$

$$4x + 2y \geq 12$$

First graph: $2x - y < 8$

$$-y < -2x + 8$$

$$y > 2x - 8$$

Next graph: $4x + 2y \geq x + 12$

$$2y \geq -4x + 12$$

$$y \geq -2x + 6$$

$y \geq -2x + 6$

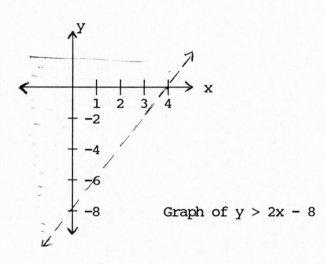

Graph of $y > 2x - 8$

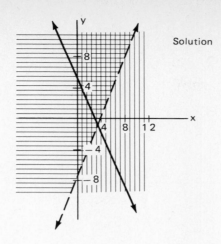

Solution

Example 2. Graph $|x| < 2$ on the Cartesian coordinate system.

Solution: Write the absolute value statement strictly as an inequality

$$|x| < 2$$

$$-2 < x < 2.$$

Example 3.   Graph $|x + 2| < 5$ means

$$-5 < x + 2 < 5$$

$$-7 < x < 3$$

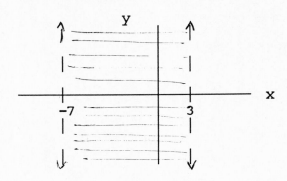

Exercise Set 4.5

Determine the solution of each system of inequalities.

1.) $x + y > 2$ 2.) $y \geq 3x$

    $y < 2x - 1$ $y \leq -4x - 2$

3.) $y < x$ 4.) $2y > 2x + 8$

    $y > 2x + 2$ $y \leq -x + 4$

5.) $|x| < 9$ 6.) $|x - 3| < 5$

7.) $|y| > 4$ 8.) $|y + 2| \leq 4$

Solution to Exercise 4.5

1.)

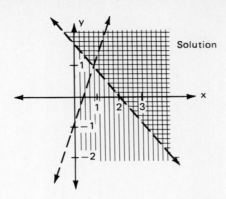

2.)

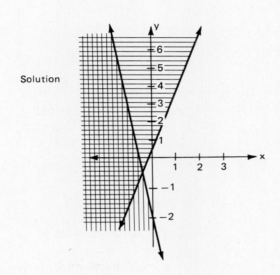

3.)

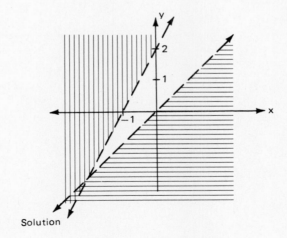

4.)

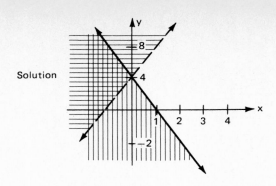

Solution

5.)

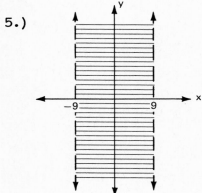

6.)

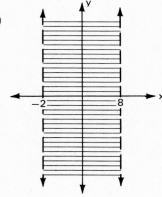

7.)

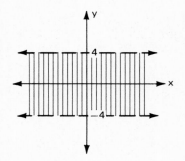

8.)

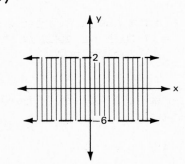

Practice Test

Write each system of equations in slope-intercept form and graph to find the solution.

1.) $-x + y = 5$

$x + y = 5$

2.) $4x + 2y = 8$

$3y = 6x + 9$

Find the solution to the system of equations by substitution.

3.) $y = 2x$

$y = 4x - 5$

4.) $3x + 3y = 9$

$-4x + 2y = 6$

Find the solution to the system of equations using the addition method.

5.) $4x - 3y = 7$

$2x + 3y = 5$

6.) $3x - 7y = 8$

$6x + 2y = 4$

Use a system of linear equations to solve problem 7.

7.) Linda has a 25% acid solution and a 50% acid solution. How much of each must she mix to get 20 liters of 45% acid solution?

Determine the solution to the system of equations using determinants.

8.) $4x - 3y = 2$

$-2x + 3y = 8$

9.) $5x + 4y + 4z = 18$

$-3x - 6y - 8z = -24$

$7x - 5y + 7z = 40$

10.) Determine the solution to the inequalities $y > 3x - 3$ and $y \leq -2x$.

Solution to Practice Test

1.) $y = x + 5$

$y = -x + 5$

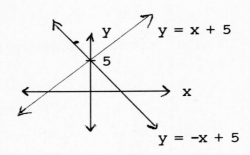

2.) $y = -2x + 4$

$y = 2x + 2$

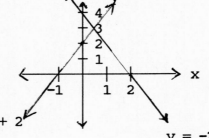

3.) (2.5, 5)

4.) (0, 3)

5.) (2, 1/3)

6.) (11/12, -3/4)

7.)   4 liters of 25% acid solution
      16 liters of 50% acid solution

8.) (5, 6)

9.) (2, -1, 3)

10.)

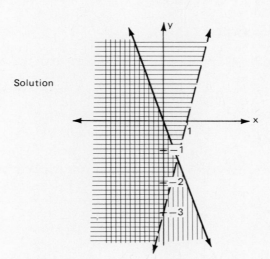

Solution

Chapter 5 Polynomials

Section 5.1 Exponents and Scientific Notation

Summary:

Product Rule for Exponents

If **m** and **n** are natural numbers and **a** is any real number, then

$$a^m \cdot a^n = a^{m+n}$$

Quotient Rule For Exponents

If **a** is any nonzero real number and **m** and **n** are nonzero integers, then

$$\frac{a^m}{a^n} = a^{m-n}$$

Negative Exponent Rule

For any nonzero real number **a** and any whole number **m**,

$$a^{-m} = \frac{1}{a^m}, \qquad a \neq 0$$

Notice that a factor can be moved from a numerator to a denominator or from a denominator to a numerator simply by changing the sign of the **exponent**.

Example 1. Simplify each expression using the rules of exponents. Write the answer without negative exponents.

a.) $x^8 x^3$ b.) $\dfrac{a^{12}}{a^5}$ c.) r^{-8} d.) $-2^2 xy^{-1}$

$x^{8+3} = x^{11}$

e.) $(-5)^2 a^{-3} bc^{-2}$ f.) $\dfrac{x^{-3} \cdot 2x^2}{x^{-5}}$

-112-

Solution: a.) $x^8x^3 = x^{8+3} = x^{11}$

b.) $\dfrac{a^{12}}{a^5} = a^{12-5} = a^7$

c.) $r^{-8} = \dfrac{1}{r^8}$

d.) $-2^2xy^{-1} = -4xy^{-1} = \dfrac{-4x}{y}$

e.) $(-5)^2a^{-3}bc^{-2} = 25 \cdot \dfrac{1}{a^3} \cdot b \cdot \dfrac{1}{c^2} = \dfrac{25b}{a^3c^2}$

f.) $\dfrac{x^{-3} \cdot 2x^2}{x^{-5}} = \dfrac{x^5 \cdot 2x^2}{x^3} = \dfrac{2x^7}{x^3} = 2x^4$

Example 2.   Simplify and write the answer without negative exponents.

$$\dfrac{8xy^{-2}}{5xy^3} \cdot \dfrac{3x^2y^2}{6x^{-1}y^3}$$

Solution: Begin by simplifing each factor without negative exponents.

$$\dfrac{8xy^{-2}}{5xy^3} \cdot \dfrac{3x^2y^2}{6x^{-1}y^3} = \dfrac{8}{5y^5} \cdot \dfrac{x^3}{2y}$$

Simplify further.

$$= \dfrac{8x^3}{10y^6}$$

$$= \dfrac{4x^3}{5y^6}$$

Summary:

To Write a Number in Scientific Notation

1. Move the decimal in the original number to the right or left until you obtain a number greater than or equal to 1 and less than 10.

2. Count the number of places you have moved the decimal to obtain the number in step 1. If the decimal was moved to the left, the count is to be considered positive. If the decimal was moved to the right, the count is to be considered negative.

3. Multiply the number obtained in step 1 by 10 raised to the count (power) found in step 2.

To Convert from a Number Given in Scientific Notation

1. Observe the exponent of the power of 10.

2. (a) If the exponent is positive, move the decimal in the number to the right the same number of places as the decimal. It may be necessary to add zeros to the number.

   (b) If the exponent is negative, move the decimal in the number to the left the same number of places as the decimal. It may be necessary to add zeros.

Example 3.   Write the following numbers using scientific notation.

   a.) 8,300 $= 8.3 \times 10^3$

   b.) 0.00012 $= 1.2 \times 10^{-4}$

   c.) 9,370,000 $= 9.37 \times 10^6$

   d.) 0.0031 $= 3.1 \times 10^{-3}$

-114-

Solution: a.) 8,300 means 8,300.0 = 8.3 x 10^3

(3 places to the left)

b.) 0.00012 = 1.2 x 10^{-4}

(4 places to the right)

c.) 9,370,000. = 9.37 x 10^6

(6 places to the left)

d.) 0.0031 = 3.1 x 10^{-2}

(2 places to the right)

Example 4. Write each number without exponents.

a.) 6.31 x 10^8 b.) 4.15 x 10^{-5} $= .00004155$

Solution: a.) Moving the decimal 8 places to the right

gives 6.31 x 10^8 = 6.31 x 100,000,000 $631,000,000$

= 631,000,000.

b.) Moving the decimal 5 places to the left

gives 4.15 x .0001 = .0000415. 4.15

Example 5. Simplify: a) $\dfrac{4.2 \times 10^8}{1.4 \times 10^{-3}}$ $\dfrac{4.2 \times 10^8}{1.4 \times 10^{-3}} = \dfrac{4.2}{1.4} \times \dfrac{10^8}{10^{-3}} = 3 \times 10^{11}$

b)   (4,000,000,000) · (83,700)

Solution: a) $\dfrac{4.2 \times 10^8}{1.4 \times 10^{-3}} = \dfrac{4.2}{1.4} \times \dfrac{10^8}{10^{-3}} = 3 \times 10^{11}$

= 300,000,000,000

$\dfrac{4.2 \times 10^8}{1.4 \times 10^{-3}} = \dfrac{4.2}{1.4} =$ $\dfrac{4.2}{1.4}$

-115-

b) (4,000,000,000) (83,700)

$$= (4 \times 10^9)(8.37 \times 10^4)$$

$$= 33.48 \times 10^{13}$$

$$= 334,800,000,000,000$$

Exercise Set 5.1

Simplify each expression using the rules of exponents.

1.) $x^3 \cdot x^2 = x^5$

2.) $\dfrac{y^7}{y^2} = y^5$

$4+3$

3.) $(-(2x)^4 x^3)(3x)$ $= (8x)(6x) = 48x^7$

4.) $(-2)^4 x^3 \cdot 3x^2$

5.) $b^3 c^2 \cdot 4b^{-1} c^{-2}$

6.) $\dfrac{f^2 g^{-2}}{f^3 g h^{-2}} = \dfrac{f^2 g^{-2}}{f^3 g h^{-2}} = \dfrac{h^2}{f g^3}$

7.) $\dfrac{q^4 r^{-5}}{q^2 r^7} = \dfrac{q^4 r^{-5}}{q^2 r^7} = \dfrac{q^2}{r^{12}}$

Simplify and write the answer without negative exponents.

8.) $\dfrac{3x^{-2} y^3}{15 x^5 y^7} \cdot \dfrac{21 x y^2}{6 x y^3} = \left(\dfrac{3x^{-2} y^3}{15 x^5 y^7}\right)\left(\dfrac{21 x y^2}{6 x y}\right) = 7$

9.) $\dfrac{8 x y^2}{3 x^3 y^3} \cdot \dfrac{6 x^4 y^3}{4 x y^5}$

10.) $\dfrac{21 a^2 b^2 c^{-3}}{85 a^3 b} \cdot \dfrac{17 a^{-3} b^2 c^{-1}}{3 a b c^{-5}}$

-116-

Write in scientific notation.

11.) 6,100,000   12.) 0.000058   13.) 1,060,000

Write each number without using exponents.

14.) 9.5×10^{-3} 15.) 6.12×10^{4} 16.) 3.2×10^{-2}

Express each number without using exponents.

17.) $\dfrac{6.3 \times 10^{5}}{2.1 \times 10^{3}}$ $= 3 \times 10^{8} =$ 18.) $\dfrac{6.4 \times 10^{3}}{1.6 \times 10^{-5}}$

19.) $(4,000,000)(0.008)$ 20.) $(3.2 \times 10^{5})(6.1 \times 10^{4})$

Solution to Exercise Set 5.1

1.) x^{5} 2.) y^{5} 3.) $-48x^{8}$ 4.) $48x^{5}$

5.) b^{2} 6.) $\dfrac{h^{2}}{fg^{3}}$ 7.) $\dfrac{q^{2}}{r^{12}}$ 8.) $\dfrac{7}{10x^{7}y^{5}}$

9.) $\dfrac{4x}{y^{3}}$ 10.) $\dfrac{7b^{2}c}{5a^{5}}$ 11.) 6.1×10^{6}

12.) 5.8×10^{-5} 13.) 1.06×10^{6} 14.) 0.0095

15.) 61,200   16.) 0.032   17.) 300

18.) 400,000,000   19.) 32000   20.) 19,520,000,000

Section 5.2 More on Exponents

Summary:

___

Zero Exponent Rule

If **a** is any nonzero real number, then

$$a^0 = 1$$

Power Rule for Exponents

If **a** is a real number and **m** and **n** are integers, then

$$a^{m\ n} = a^{m \cdot n} \qquad \text{Power Rule 1}$$

Power Rules for Exponents

If **a** and **b** are real numbers and **m** is an integer, then

$$ab^{\ m} = a^m b^m \qquad \text{Power Rule 2}$$

$$\frac{a}{b}^{\ m} = \frac{a^m}{b^m}, \ b \neq 0 \qquad \text{Power Rule 3}$$

___

Example 1. Evaluate the following. Assume all bases represented by variables are non-zero.

a.) b^0

b.) $-12x^0$

c.) $(x + y)^0$

d.) $(-4x)^0$

e.) $5a^0 - 6b^0$

Solution: a.) $b^0 = 1$

b.) $-12x^0 = -12(1) = -12$

c.) $(x + y)^0 = 1$

d.) $(-4x)^0 = (-4)^0 x^0 = 1 \cdot 1 = 1$

e.) $5a^0 - 6b^0 = 5(1) - 6(1) = 5 - 6 = -1$

Example 2.   Simplify and write without negative exponents.

a.) $(2x^3)^2$

b.) $(x^2 y^3)^4$

c.) $\dfrac{x^2}{y}^3$

Solution: a.) $(2x^3)^2 = 2^2 (x^3)^2 = 4x^6$

b.) $(x^2 y^3)^4 = (x^2)^4 (y^3)^4 = x^8 y^{12}$

c.) $\dfrac{x^2}{y}^3 = \dfrac{(x^2)^3}{(y)^3} = \dfrac{x^6}{y^3}$

Exercise Set 5.2

Evaluate. Assume all bases represented by variables are non-zero.

1.) $5x^0$ 2.) $-(8x^0)$ 3.) $-(3x)^0$ 4.) $4(x + y)^0$

Simplify and write without negative exponents.

5.) $(8a^2)^3$ 6.) $(4x^2 y)^5$ 7.) $(2x^3 y^5)^3$

8.) $\dfrac{16xy}{2x^2}^2$ 9.) $\dfrac{x^3}{y^2}^4$ 10.) $\dfrac{2x}{3y}^4$

Solution to Exercise Set 5.2

1.) 5   2.) -8   3.) -1   4.) 4

5.) $512a^6$ 6.) $1024x^{10}y^5$ 7.) $8x^9y^{15}$ 8.) $\dfrac{64y^2}{x^2}$

9.) $\dfrac{x^{12}}{y^8}$ 10.) $\dfrac{16x^4}{81y^4}$

Section 5.3 Addition and Subtraction of Polynomials

Summary:

A **polynomial** is a finite sum of terms in which all variables have whole-number exponents and no variables appear in denominators.

Example 1. State whether each of the following is a polynomial.

a.) $x + 3$

b.) $2x^2 + x^{\frac{1}{2}} + 5$

c.) $5x^2 - 7$

Solution: a.) Polynomial

b.) Not a polynomial because of $x^{\frac{1}{2}}$.

c.) Polynomial

Summary:

The **degree** of a term is the sum of the exponents on the variables in the term. Thus, $3x^2y^3z$ is of degree 6 (that is $2 + 3 + 1 = 6$).

The **degree of a polynomial** is the same as that of its highest-degree term.

Example 2. Write the polynomial in descending order of the variable. Give the degree of each polynomial.

a.) $x^3 + 5 - 6x + x^2$

b.) $8x^5 - 2x + 5x^9$

c.) $5x^3 - 2x^2 + 4$

Solution: a.) $x^3 + x^2 - 6x + 5$, third degree.

b.) $5x^9 + 8x^5 - 2x$, ninth degree.

c.) $5x^3 - 2x^2 + 4$, third degree.

Summary:

Adding Polynomials

To add polynomials, combine the like terms of the polynomials.

Example 3. Simplify $(5x^2 - 2x + 1) + (3x^2 - 8x + 2)$.

Solution: $(5x^2 - 2x + 1) + (3x^2 - 8x + 2)$

Remove parentheses: $5x^2 - 2x + 1 + 3x^2 - 8x + 2$

Rearrange terms: $5x^2 + 3x^2 - 2x - 8x + 1 + 2$

Combine like terms: $8x^2 - 10x + 3$

Summary:

To Subtract Polynomials

1. Remove parenthes from polynomial being subtracted, and change the sign of every term of the polynomial being subtracted.

2. Combine like terms.

Example 4. Simplify $(5x^2 - 8x + 2) - (-2x^2 + 4x - 5)$.

Solution: $(5x^2 - 8x + 2) - (-2x^2 + 4x - 5)$

Remove parentheses and change sign of each term being subtracted:

$$5x^2 - 8x + 2 + 2x^2 - 4x + 5$$

Rearrange terms: $5x^2 + 2x^2 - 8x - 4x + 2 + 5$

Combine like terms: $7x^2 - 12x + 7$

Example 5.   Subtract $5x^3 - 2x + 4$ from $8x^2 - 2x + 7$.

Solution: $(8x^2 - 2x + 7) - (5x^3 - 2x + 4)$

$\qquad\qquad 8x^2 - 2x + 7 - 5x^3 + 2x - 4$

$\qquad\qquad -5x^3 + 8x^2 - 2x + 2x + 7 - 4$

$\qquad\qquad -5x^3 + 8x^2 + 3$

Exercise Set 5.3

State whether each of the following is a polynomial.

1.) $x + 5$

2.) $.5x^2 - 3x + 2$

3.) $x^2 + 2x^{.5} - 9$

State the degree of the following polynomials.

4.) $8x + 7$

5.) $-3x^3 + 2x + 4$

6.) $7x^2 - 9x + 12$

Simplify the following by performing the indicated operation.

7.) $(8x^3 - 2x^2 + 4x + 5) + (2x^3 + 3x^2 - 2x - 5)$

8.) $(-4x^2 + 2x - 9) + (5x^3 - 2x^2 + 4x + 7)$

9.) $(3x^3 - 7x^2 + x - 5) - (x^3 - 2x^2 + 3x - 9)$

10.) $(5x^4 - 6x^2 + x - 9) - (5x^3 - 6x^2 + x + 9)$

-123-

Solution to Exercise Set 5.3

1.) Polynomial   2.) Polynomial

3.) Not a polynomial   4.) First degree

5.) Third degree   6.) Second degree

7.) $10x^3 + x^2 + 2x$ 8.) $5x^3 - 6x^2 + 6x - 2$

9.) $2x^3 - 5x^2 - 2x + 4$ 10.) $5x^4 - 5x^3 - 18$

Section 5.4 Multiplication of Polynomials

Summary:

Distributive Property

$$a(b + c + d + \ldots + n) = ab + ac + ad + \ldots + an$$

Example 1. Multiply

     a.) $2x(5x + 2)$

     b.) $3x^2(5x^3 - 6x - 9)$

     c.) $-3xy(2xy - 3x + 4y + 1)$

Solution:　a.) $2x(5x + 2) = (2x)(5x) + (2x)(2)$

$$= 10x^2 + 4x$$

b.) $3x^2(5x^3 - 6x - 9)$

$$= (3x^2)(5x^3) + (3x^2)(-6x) + (3x^2)(-9)$$

$$= 15x^5 - 18x^3 - 27x^2$$

c.) $-3xy(2xy - 3x + 4y + 1)$

$$= (-3xy)(2xy) + (-3xy)(-3x)$$

$$+ (-3xy)(4y) + (-3xy)(1)$$

$$= -6x^2y^2 + 9x^2y - 12xy^2 - 3xy$$

Summary:

Multiply a Binomial by a Binomial

$$(a + b)(c + d) = ac + ad + bc + bd$$

Square of a Binomial

$$(a + b)^2 = a^2 + 2ab + b^2$$

$$(a - b)^2 = a^2 - 2ab + b^2$$

Product of Sum and Difference of the Same Two Terms

$$(a + b)(a - b) = a^2 - b^2$$

Example 2. Multiply $(4x + 5)(3y - 2)$

Solution: $(4x + 5)(3y - 2)$

$$= (4x)(3y) + (4x)(-2) + (5)(3y) + (5)(-2)$$

$$= 12xy - 8x + 15y - 10$$

Example 3. Expand a.) $(2x + 3)^2$

b.) $(x - 2y)^2$

Solution: a.) $(2x + 3)^2 = (2x)^2 + 2(2x)(3) + (3)^2$

$$= 4x^2 + 12x + 9$$

b.) $(x - 2y)^2 = x^2 - 2(x)(2y) + (2y)^2$

$$= x^2 - 4xy + 4y^2$$

Example 4. Multiply $[2a - (3b + c)][2a + (3b + c)]$

Solution: $[2a - (3b + c)][2a + (3b + c)]$

$$= (2a)^2 - (3b + c)^2 = 4a^2 - (9b^2 + 6bc + c^2)$$

$$= 4a^2 - 9b^2 - 6bc - c^2$$

Exercise Set 5.4

Multiply as indicated.

1.) $3(x + 2) =$
     $3x + 6$

2.) $3x(-4x + 2)$

3.) $3x(2x^2 + 8x - 4)$

4.) $-2x^2y(3x^2 + 2xy - y^2)$

5.) $(3x + 5)(2x + 7)$

6.) $(4x - y)(3x + y)$

7.) $(q + r)(s + t)$

8.) $(3xy - 2y)(4xy - 3x)$

Multiply using either the square of a binomial procedure or the difference of two squares procedures.

9.) $(x + 2)^2 = x^2 + 4x + 4$

10.) $(x + 2)(x - 2) = x^2 + 4$

11.) $(3x^2 - 2y)^2$

12.) $(4a - 2b)(4a + 2b)$

13.) $(2x^3 - 3y)^2$

14.) $[a - (2b + c)][a + (2b + c)]$

15.) $[a + (2b + c)][a - (2b - c)]$

Solution to Exercise Set 5.4

1.) $3x + 6$

2.) $-12x^2 + 6x$

3.) $6x^3 + 24x^2 - 12x$

4.) $-6x^4y - 4x^3y^2 + 2x^2y^3$

5.) $6x^2 + 31x + 35$

6.) $12x^2 + xy - y^2$

7.) $qs + qt + rs + rt$

8.) $12x^2y^2 - 9x^2y - 8xy^2 + 6xy$

9.) $x^2 + 4x + 4$

10.) $x^2 - 4$

11.) $9x^4 - 12x^2y + 4y^2$ 12.) $16a^2 - 4b^2$

13.) $4x^6 - 12x^3y + 9y^2$ 14.) $a^2 - 4b^2 + 4bc + c^2$

15.) $a^2 - 4b^2 + c^2$

Section 5.5 Division of Polynomials

Summary:

To divide a polynomial by a monomial, divide each term of the polymonial by the monomial.

Example 1. Divide $\dfrac{15x^2 - 21x}{3x}$.

Solution: $\dfrac{15x^2 - 21x}{3x} = \dfrac{15x^2}{3x} - \dfrac{21x}{3x} = 5x - 7$

Example 2. Divide $\dfrac{10x^3 - 8x + 2x - 1}{2x}$

Solution: $\dfrac{10x^3 - 8x + 2x - 1}{2x} = \dfrac{10x^3}{2x} - \dfrac{8x^2}{2x} + \dfrac{2x}{2x} - \dfrac{1}{2x}$

$= 5x^2 - 4x + 1 - \dfrac{1}{2x}$

Example 3.   Divide $\dfrac{x^2 - 8x + 15}{3 - x}$

Solution: Rewrite the problem as a long division.

$$x - 3 \,\overline{\big)\, x^2 - 8x + 15}$$

Divide x^2 (the first term in $x^2 - 8x + 15$) by x (the first term in $x - 3$).

Place the quotient, x, above the term containing x in the divisor.

$$\begin{array}{r} x \\ x - 3 \,\overline{\big)\, x^2 - 8x + 15} \end{array}$$

Next, multiply the x by $x - 3$ as you would do in long division and place the product under like terms.

$$\begin{array}{r} x \\ x - 3 \,\overline{\big)\, x^2 - 8x + 15} \\ x^2 - 3x \end{array}$$

Subtract $x^2 - 3x$ from $x^2 - 8x$ by changing the

signs of $x^2 - 3x$ and adding.

$$\begin{array}{r} x \\ x - 3 \,\overline{\big)\, x^2 - 8x + 15} \\ x^2 - 3x \\ 5x \end{array}$$

Next, bring down 15.

$$\begin{array}{r} x \\ x - 3 \,\overline{\big)\, x^2 - 8x + 15} \\ x^2 - 3x \\ 5x + 15 \end{array}$$

Find the quotient of 5x divided by x. The quotient is +5. Place the +5 above the constant in the dividend and multiply 5 by x - 3.

$$
\begin{array}{r}
x + 5 \\
x - 3 \overline{\smash{\big)}\ x^2 - 8x + 15} \\
\underline{x^2 - 3x} \\
5x + 15 \\
\underline{5x + 15}
\end{array}
$$

Finally, finish the problem by subtracting.

$$
\begin{array}{r}
x + 5 \\
x - 3 \overline{\smash{\big)}\ x^2 - 8x + 15} \\
\underline{x^2 - 3x} \\
5x + 15 \\
\underline{5x + 15} \\
0
\end{array}
$$

Note:

_____

When you are dividing a polynomial by a binomial, you should list both the polynomial and binomial in descending order. If a given powered term is missing, it is often helpful to include that term with a numerical coefficient of 0.

_____

Example 4. Divide $\dfrac{x^3 - 27}{x - 3}$

Solution: $\dfrac{x^3 - 27}{x - 3}$

$$x - 3 \overline{\smash{\big)}\ x^3 - 27}$$

Rewrite $x^3 - 27$ as $x^3 + 0x^2 + 0x - 27$.

$$x - 3 \overline{\smash{\big)}\ x^3 + 0x^2 + 0x - 27}$$

Proceed as outlined in Example 3.

$$
\begin{array}{r}
x^2 + 3x + 9 \\
x - 3 \overline{\smash{\big)}\ x^3 + 0x^2 + 0x - 27} \\
\underline{x^3 - 3x^2} \\
3x^2 + 0x \\
\underline{3x^2 - 9x} \\
9x - 27 \\
\underline{9x - 27} \\
0
\end{array}
$$

Exercise Set 5.5

Divide.

1.) $\dfrac{a^3 + 6a^2 + a}{a}$

2.) $\dfrac{6x^4 - 9x^2 + 3x}{3x}$

3.) $\dfrac{8x^2y + 2xy - 6xy^2}{2xy}$

4.) $\dfrac{12x^2 - 20x + 5}{2x}$

5.) $\dfrac{x^2 + 12x + 35}{x + 5}$

6.) $\dfrac{x^2 - 3x - 18}{x + 3}$

7.) $\dfrac{x^2 - 16}{x - 4}$

8.) $\dfrac{4x^2 - 64}{2x + 8}$

9.) $\dfrac{27x^3 - 8}{3x - 2}$

10.) $\dfrac{8x^3 + 1}{2x + 1}$

Solution to Exercise Set 5.5

1.) $a^2 + 6a + 1$

2.) $2x^3 - 3x + 1$

3.) $4x + 1 - 3y$

4.) $6x - 10 + \dfrac{5}{2x}$

5.) $x + 7$

6.) $x - 6$

7.) $x + 4$

8.) $2x - 8$

9.) $9x^2 + 6x + 4$

10.) $4x^2 - 2x + 1$

Section 5.6 Synthetic Division (optional)

Summary:

When a polynomial is divided by a binomial of the form $x - a$, the division process can be greatly shortened by a process called **synthetic division**. In synthetic division, the variables are not written since they do not play a role in determining the numerical coefficients of the quotient.

Example 1. Use synthetic division to divide.

$$(4x^3 - 6x^2 + 8x + 2) \div (x - 2)$$

Solution: Write the dividend in descending powers of x. Then list the numerical coefficients of each term in the dividend. If a power is missing place a 0 in the appropriate position to serve as a place holder.

$$4 \quad -6 \quad 8 \quad 2$$

When dividing by a binomial of the form $x - a$, place $\underline{|a}$ to the right of the line of numbers representing the numerical coefficients of the dividend.

$$4 \quad -6 \quad 8 \quad 2 \quad \underline{|2}$$

Bring down the left hand number.

$$
\begin{array}{ccccc}
4 & -6 & 8 & 2 & \underline{|2} \\
& 8 & & & \\
\hline
4 & 2 & & &
\end{array}
$$

Multiply 2 · 2 (the value of a) to get 4.
Place 4 under the 8, then add 8 and 4 to get 12.

$$
\begin{array}{ccccc}
4 & -6 & 8 & 2 & \underline{|2} \\
& 8 & 4 & & \\
\hline
4 & 2 & 12 & &
\end{array}
$$

-132-

Multiply 12 · 2 (the value of a) to get 24.
Place 24 under the 2. Add 2 and 24 to get 26.

$$
\begin{array}{rrrr}
4 & -6 & 8 & 2 \\
  & 8 & 4 & 24 \\
\hline
4 & 2 & 12 & 26
\end{array}
$$

The quotient must be one degree less than the dividend. Since the dividend was a third-degree polynomial, the quotient is a second-degree polynomial with numerical coefficients as written in the bottom line of the synthetic division.

The quotient is therefore $4x^2 + 2x + 12 + \dfrac{26}{x - 2}$

Example 2. Use synthetic division to divide.

$(2x^5 - 3x^2 - 7x + 9) \div (x + 3)$

Solution: Recall we must be dividing by x - a.
Therefore, rewrite x + 3 as x - (-3).
The value of **a** is -3.

Starting with
$$
\begin{array}{rrrrrr|r}
2 & 0 & 0 & -3 & -7 & 9 & \underline{-3} \\
\hline
2 & & & & &
\end{array}
$$

Step 2.
$$
\begin{array}{rrrrrr|r}
2 & 0 & 0 & -3 & -7 & 9 & \underline{-3} \\
  & -6 & & & & \\
\hline
2 & -6 & & & &
\end{array}
$$

Step 3.
$$
\begin{array}{rrrrrr|r}
2 & 0 & 0 & -3 & -7 & 9 & \underline{-3} \\
  & -6 & 18 & & & \\
\hline
2 & -6 & 18 & & &
\end{array}
$$

Step 4.
$$
\begin{array}{rrrrrr|r}
2 & 0 & 0 & -3 & -7 & 9 & \underline{-3} \\
  & -6 & 18 & -54 & & \\
\hline
2 & -6 & 18 & -57 & &
\end{array}
$$

Step 5.
$$
\begin{array}{rrrrrr|r}
2 & 0 & 0 & -3 & -7 & 9 & \underline{-3} \\
  & -6 & 18 & -54 & 171 & \\
\hline
2 & -6 & 18 & -57 & 164 &
\end{array}
$$

Step 6.
$$
\begin{array}{rrrrrr|r}
2 & 0 & 0 & -3 & -7 & 9 & \underline{-3} \\
  & -6 & 18 & -54 & 171 & -492 \\
\hline
2 & -6 & 18 & -57 & 164 & -483
\end{array}
$$

The quotient is:

$$2x^4 - 6x^3 + 18x^2 - 57x + 164 - \dfrac{483}{x + 3}$$

-133-

Exercise Set 5.6

Divide using synthetic division.

1.) $(x^2 + 15x + 56) \div (x - 7)$

2.) $(3x^3 - 4x^2 + 7x) \div 9) - (x - 3)$

3.) $(15x^3 - 2x + 7) \div (x + 5)$

4.) $(4x^3 + 2x^2 - 8x + 5) \div (x - 3)$

5.) $(x^3 - 8) - (x - 2)$

Solution to Exercise Set 5.6

1.) $x + 22 + \dfrac{210}{x - 7}$

2.) $3x^2 + 5x + 22 + \dfrac{57}{x - 3}$

3.) $15x^2 - 75x + 373 - \dfrac{1858}{x + 5}$

4.) $4x^2 + 14x + 34 + \dfrac{107}{x - 3}$

5.) $x^2 + 2x + 4$

Section 5.7 Polynomial Functions

Summary:

Polynomial Function (General Form)

$$f(x) = a_n x^n + a_{n-1} x^{n-1} + a_{n-2} x^{n-2} + a_{n-3} x^{n-3} + \ldots + a_1 x + a_0$$

where all exponents on x are whole numbers and

$a_n, a_{n-1}, a_{n-2}, \ldots, a_1, a_0$ are all real numbers with $a_n \neq 0$.

To evaluate a polynomial function for a specific value of the variable, substitute the value in the function whenever the variable appears.

Example 1. $f(x) = 3x + 2$

Evaluate a.) $f(2)$ b.) $f(-3)$

Solution: a.) $f(x) = 3x + 2$

$f(2) = 3(2) + 2$

$= 6 + 2$

$= 8$

b.) $f(x) = 3x + 2$

$f(-3) = 3(-3) + 2$

$= -9 + 2$

$= -7$

Example 2. $f(x) = x^2 + 2x + 1$

Find   a.) $f(2)$ b.) $f(a)$ c.) $f(a + 2)$

Solution: a.) $f(x) = x^2 + 2x + 1$

$f(2) = 2^2 + 2(2) + 1$

$= 4 + 4 + 1$

$= 9$

b.) $f(x) = x^2 + 2x + 1$

$f(a) = a^2 + 2a + 1$

c.) $f(a + 2) = (a + 2)^2 + 2(a + 2) + 1$

$= (a^2 + 2a + 4) + (2a + 4) + 1$

$= a^2 + 4a + 9$

Example 3. The Three-dollar Book Club allows you to buy each book for $3 plus a total shipping cost of $2. If the total price **(p)** on a shipment of **n** books can be written as $p = f(n) = \$3n + \$2$, find **p** for:

       a.) 10 books   b.) 17 books

Solution: a.) $p = f(n) = \$3n + 2$

$$p = f(10) = \$3(10) + \$2$$

$$= \$30 + \$2$$

$$= \$32$$

         b.) $p = f(n) = \$3n + \$2$

$$p = f(17) = \$3(17) + \$2$$

$$= \$51 + \$2$$

$$= \$53$$

Exercise Set 5.7

1.) $f(x) = 5x - 7$;   find   a.) $f(2)$ b.) $f(5)$

2.) $f(x) = -3x + 4$;   find   a.) $f(-2)$ b.) $f(4)$

3.) $f(x) = -7x + 8$;   find   a.) $f(0)$ b.) $f(n)$

4.) $f(x) = x^2 + 2$;   find   a.) $f(2)$ b.) $f(\tfrac{1}{2})$

5.) $f(x) = 9x^2 + 3x + 2$; find   a.) $f\,\dfrac{1}{3}$ b.) $f\,\dfrac{2}{3}$

6.) $f(x) = -3x^2 + 4x + 5$; find   a.) $f(1)$ b.) $f(7)$

7.) $f(x) = x^2 - 1$;   find   a.) $f(y)$ b.) $f(y + 1)$

8.) $f(x) = 3x^2 + 2x$;   find   a.) $f(c)$ b.) $f(c + d)$

9.) The sum **s** of the first **n** odd counting number is given

by the function s = f(n) = n^2, find s when:

    a.) n = 2   b.) n = 10

10.) The distance **s**, in meters, that a falling body travels under earth's gravitational pull is defined by the amount of time, **t** in seconds, that the body falls in the function

$$s = f(t) = 9.8t^2, \text{ find } s \text{ when:}$$

                                      a.) t = 1

                                      b.) t = 2

Solution to Exercise Set 5.7

1. a) 3   b) 18

2. a) 10   b) -8

3. a) 8   b) -7n + 8

4. a) 6   b) 2¼

5. a) 4   b) 8

6. a) 6   b) -114

7. a) $y^2 - 1$ b) $y^2 + 2y$

8. a) $3c^2 + 2c$ b) $3c^2 + 6cd + 3d^2 + 2c + 2d$

9. a) 4   b) 100

10. a) 9.8m   b) 39.2m

Section 5.8 Graphing Polynomial Functions

Summary:

To graph polynomial functions we can substitute values of **x**, find corresponding values of **y** and plot the points on the Cartesian coordinate system.

The first function we will graph in this section is a quadratic function.

Quadratic Function

Any function of the form

$$f(x) = ax^2 + bx + c, \qquad a \neq 0$$

where **a**, **b** and **c** are real numbers, is a **quadratic function**.

In the quadratic function, if **"a"** is positive, the graph opens upward and has a lowest point called the vertex on the axis of symmetry.

If the value of **"a"** is negative, the graph opens downward and has a highest point called the vertex on the axis of symmetry.

Axis of Symmetry

Given an equation of the form $y = ax^2 + bx + c$, its graph will be a parabola with axis of symmetry.

$$x = \frac{-b}{2a}$$

Example 1. Graph $f(x) = 2x^2 + 8x - 1$; a = 2, b = 8, c = -1.

Solution: Since the coefficient of the squared term is 2, which is a positive number, this parabola will open upward. Now find the axis of symmetry.

$$x = \frac{-b}{2a} = \frac{-8}{2(2)} = \frac{-8}{4} = -2$$

The parabola is symmetric about the line x = -2. We will choose values of x near -2.

-138-

We form a table of values of x and y by picking x values near -2 and finding the corresponding y values.

x	y
-5	9
-4	-1
-3	-7
-2	-9
-1	-7
0	-1
1	9

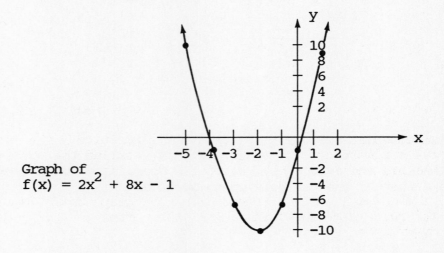

Graph of
$f(x) = 2x^2 + 8x - 1$

Note that the vertex (-2, -9) of the graph

$f(x) = 2x^2 + 8x - 1$ is the lowest point on

the graph and is on the axis of symmetry

x = -2.

Summary:

To graph third-degree or higher functions accurately requires a knowledge of calculus. However, it is sufficient for our needs to substitute values for **x**, find corresponding values for **y** and plot the points on the Cartesian coordinate system.

Example 2.   Graph $x^3 - 2x^2 - x + 2$

Solution: Pick values for **x** and calculate corresponding
values for **y**.

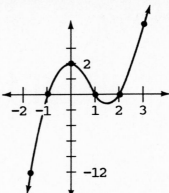

x	y
-2	-12
-1	0
0	2
1	0
2	0
1.5	-0.625
3	8

Exercise Set 5.8

Indicate the axis of symmetry, the coordinates of the vertex
and whether the parabola opens up or down.

1.) $y = 3x^2 + 6x - 9$

2.) $y = x^2 + 2x + 4$

3.) $y = -3x^2 - 9x + 1$

4.) $y = -x^2 - x + 1$

Graph the quadratic function.

5.) $y = x^2 + 2x + 1$

6.) $y = x^2 - 4$

7.) $y = 3x^2 + 6x - 9$

8.) $y = 4x^2 - 4$

Graph the cubic equations.

9.) $y = x^3 + 3x^2 - x - 3$

10.) $y = x^3 + x^2 - x - 1$

Solution to Exercise Set 5.8

	Axis of symmetry	Vertex	Opens
1.)	-1	(-1, -12)	Upward
2.)	-2	(-2, 4)	Upward
3.)	-1.5	(1.5, -19.25)	Downward
4.)	- .5	(-.5, 1.25)	Downward

5.) $y = x^2 + 2x + 1$

x	y
-3	4
-2	1
-1	0
0	1
1	4
2	9

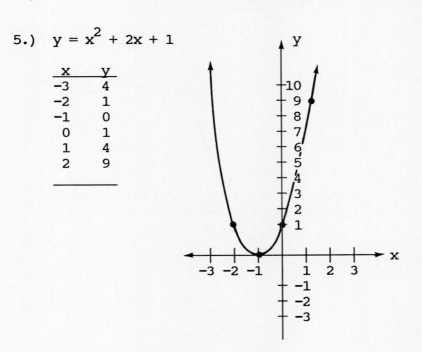

6.) $y = x^2 - 4$

x	y
-3	5
-2	0
-1	-3
0	-4
1	-3
2	0
3	5

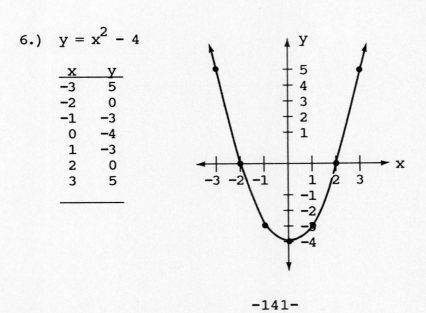

7.) $y = 3x^2 + 6x - 9$

x	y
−4	15
−3	0
−2	− 9
−1	−12
0	− 9
1	0
2	15

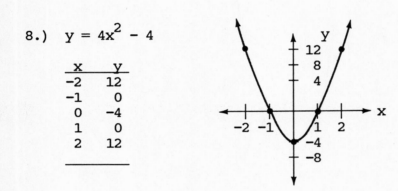

8.) $y = 4x^2 - 4$

x	y
−2	12
−1	0
0	−4
1	0
2	12

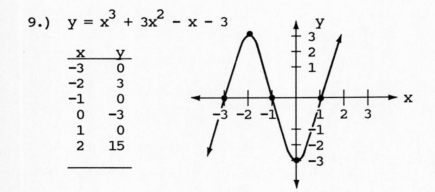

9.) $y = x^3 + 3x^2 - x - 3$

x	y
−3	0
−2	3
−1	0
0	−3
1	0
2	15

10.) $y = x^3 + x^2 - x - 1$

x	y
-2	-3
-1	0
0	-1
1	0
2	9

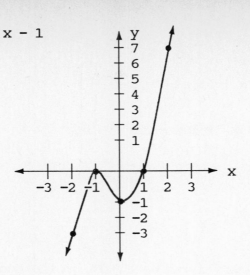

Practice Test

Simplify and write the answer without negative exponents.

1.) $\dfrac{5x^2y}{3xy^{-2}} \cdot \dfrac{6xy^{-2}}{10x^2y^3}$

2.) $\dfrac{2x^3y^2}{3x^{-4}}^2$

Write in scientific notation.

3.) 8,510,000 $= 8.5 \times 10^6$

4.) 0.00013 $= 1.3 \times 10^{-4}$

5.) $(8.1 \times 10^{13})(6.3 \times 10^{-7})$

$\dfrac{8.1 \times 10^{13}}{6.3 \times 10^{-7}} = \dfrac{8.1}{6.3} \times \dfrac{10^{13}}{10^{-7}} = 1.3 \times 10^6 =$

1,300,000

Perform the indicated operation.

6.) $(-8x^3 + 7x^2 - 3x - 5) + (7x^3 - 2x + 7)$

6.) $\begin{array}{r} -8x^3 + 7x^2 - 3x - 5 \\ 7x^3 - 2x + 7 \\ \hline x^3 + 7x^2 - 5x + 2 \end{array}$

7.) $(3x^4 + 7x^3 - 8x - 9) - (-2x^3 + 2x^2 - 7x + 5)$

6.) $-3x + 7x^2 - 5x + 2$

-143-

7.) $3x^4 + 9x^5 - 2x^2 - 14$

8.) $(2x + 6)(x - 4)$

9.) $(-3x^2 - 2x + 5)(x - 9)$

10.) $(20x^3 - 75x^2 + 10x - 35) \div (5x)$

11.) $5x^2y^3(6x^3y + 4x^2y^2 - 3xy^3 + 8)$

12.) $(5x^3 - 6x^2 + 4x - 9) \div (x - 3)$

13.) Use synthetic division to obtain the quotient.

$(4x^2 - 3x + 5) \div (x - 2)$

If $f(x) = -2x^2 + 3x - 6$, find:

14.) $f(-2)$ 15.) $f(3)$

16.) $f(a)$ 17.) $f(a + 2)$

18.) Graph $f(x) = x^2 - 1$

19.) Graph $f(x) = x^2 + 5x + 6$

20.) Graph $f(x) = x^3 + x^2 - 4x - 4$

Solution to Practice Test

1.) $\dfrac{1}{y^2}$ 2.) $\dfrac{4x^{14}}{9y^4}$

3.) 8.51×10^6 4.) 1.3×10^{-4}

5.) 5.103×10^7 6.) $-x^3 + 7x^2 - 5x + 2$

7.) $3x^4 + 9x^3 - 2x^2 - x - 14$ 8.) $2x^2 - 2x - 24$

9.) $-3x^3 - 25x^2 + 23x - 45$ 10.) $4x^2 - 15x + 2 - \dfrac{7}{x}$

11.) $30x^5 + 20x^4y^5 - 15x^3y^6 + 40x^2y^3$

12.) $5x^2 + 9x + 31 + \dfrac{84}{x - 3}$ 13.) $4x + 5 + \dfrac{15}{x - 2}$

14.) -20 15.) -15

16.) $-2a^2 + 3a - 6$ 17.) $-2a^2 - 5a - 8$

18.)
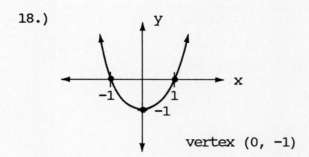
vertex $(0, -1)$

19.)
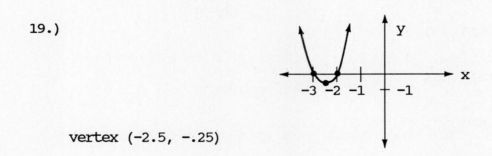
vertex $(-2.5, -.25)$

20.)
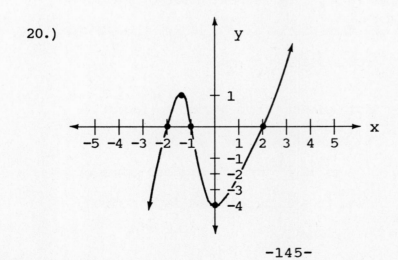

Chapter 6   Factoring

Section 6.1   Factoring a Monomial from a Polynomial and
                 Factoring by Grouping.

Summary:

The **greatest common factor** (GCF) of two or more expressions
is the largest factor that divides (without remainder) each
expression.

Example 1.   Find the GCF of the following terms:

   a.) a^5, a^6, a^3, a^9

   b.) $x^3 y^2$, $x^2 y^4$, $x^5 y^7$

   c.) $6a^2 b^2$, $10a^2 b^3$, $14ab^3$

   d.) $5(y - 2)^2$, $7(y - 2)^3$, $8(y-2)^4$

Solution: a.)   The GCF is a^3 since a^3 is the highest power

                    of **a** that divides each term.

              b.)   The highest power of **x** common to all three

                    terms is x^2. The highest power of **y** common

                    to all three terms is y^2. Thus, the GCF is

                    $x^2 y^2$ for all three terms.

              c.)   The coefficients have a common factor of

                    2. The highest power of **a** common to all

                    three terms is a^1 and the highest power of

                    b common to all three terms is b^2. Thus,

                    the GCF is $2ab^2$.

-146-

d.) The coefficients have a common factor of
1. The highest power of $(y - 2)$ is $(y - 2)^2$.
Thus, the GCF is $1(y - 2)^3$ or just $(y - 2)^2$.

Summary:

To Factor a Monomial from a Polynomial

1. Determine the greatest common factor of all terms in the polynomial.

2. Write each term as the product of the GCF and its other factors.

3. Use the distributive property to **factor out the GCF.**

Example 2.   Factor.

   a.) $12x^3 + 6x^5 - 8x^4$

   b.) $7x^2y^3 + 42x^3y^2 - 28x^2y^2$

   c.) $12x^2(3y - 2) - 8x^3(3y - 2)$

Solution: a.)   The GCF is $2x^3$

$12x^3 + 6x^5 - 8x^4$

$= 2x^3 \cdot 6 + 2x^3 \cdot 3x^2 + 2x^3 \cdot (-4x)$

$= 2x^3(6 + 3x^2 - 4x)$

   b.)   The GCF is $7x^2y^2$

$7x^2y^3 + 42x^3y^2 - 28x^2y^2$

$= 7x^2y^2 \cdot y + 7x^2y^2 \cdot 6x + 7x^2y^2 \cdot (-4)$

$= 7x^2y^2(y + 6x - 4)$

c.) The GCF is $4x^2(3y - 2)$

$$12x^2(3y - 2) - 8x^3(3y - 2)$$

$$= 4x^2(3y - 2) \cdot 3 + 4x^2(3y - 2) \cdot (-2x)$$

$$= 4x(3y - 2)(3 - 2x)$$

Summary:

To Factor by Grouping

1. Arrange the four terms into two groups of two terms each. Each group of two terms must have a GCF.

2. Factor the GCF from each group of two terms.

3. If the two terms formed in Step 2 have a GCF, factor out that GCF.

Example 3. Factor $2x^2 + 16x + 14x + 112$ by grouping.

Solution: Factor 2 from all the terms.

$$2x^2 + 16x + 14x + 112 = 2(x^2 + 8x + 7x + 56)$$

Next, factor **x** from the first two terms of the polynomial and 7 from the last two terms of the polynomial.

$$= 2[x(x + 8) + 7(x + 8)]$$

Next, factor $(x + 8)$ from the two terms within the brackets.

$$= 2[(x + 7)(x + 8)]$$

Exercise Set 6.1

Factor out the greatest common factor.

1.) $3a^3 + 6a^5 - 7a^6$

2.) $12a^2b + 18ab^2 + 24a^2b^2$

3.) $-8x^2y^3 - 24x^3y^4 + 12x^3y^3$

4.) $9x^2 - 3x^3 + 12x^4$

5.) $8x(x + 2y) - 7(x + 2y)$

6.) $x(x - y) - y(x - y)$

Factor by grouping.

7.) $x^2 - 8x + 5x - 40$

8.) $x^2 + 3x - 3x - 9$

9.) $x^2 + 6x + 3x + 18$

10.) $x^2 - 12x + 2x - 24$

Solution to Exercise Set 6.1

1.) $a^3(3 + 6a^2 - 7a^3)$ 2.) $6ab(2a + 3b + 4ab)$

3.) $-4x^2y^3(2 + 6xy - 3x)$ 4.) $3x^2(3 - x + 4x^2)$

5.) $(8x - 7)(x + 2y)$ 6.) $(x - y)^2$

7.) $(x + 5)(x - 8)$ 8.) $(x - 3)(x + 3)$

9.) $(x + 3)(x + 6)$ 10.) $(x + 2)(x - 12)$

Section 6.2 Factoring Trinomials

Summary:

To Factor Trinomials of the Form $x^2 + bx + c$ (note a = 1)

1. Find two numbers (or factors) whose product is **c**, and whose sum is **b**.

2. The factors of the trinomial will be of the form

$$(x \quad)(x \quad)$$

one factor   other factor
determined   determined
in Step 1   in Step 1

Example 1.   Factor $x^2 - 9x + 14$

Solution: We must find two numbers whose product is 14 and whose sum is -9. The numbers are -2 and -7.

$$x^2 - 9x + 14 = (x - 2)(x - 7)$$

Example 2.   Factor $4x^2 + 4x - 48$

Solution: First, factor 4 from all three terms.

$$4x^2 + 4x - 48 = 4(x^2 + x - 12)$$

Now, factor $x^2 + x - 12$ by finding two numbers whose product is -12 and whose sum is +1. The numbers are +4 and -3.

$$= 4(x^2 + x - 12)$$

$$= 4(x + 4)(x - 3)$$

Therefore, $4x^2 + 4x - 48 = 4(x + 4)(x - 3)$.

Summary:

To Factor Trinomials of the Form $ax^2 + bx + c$,
       $a \neq 1$, Using Grouping

1. Find two numbers whose product is **a** · **c** and whose sum is **b**.

2. Rewrite the **bx** term using the numbers found in Step 1.

3. Factor by grouping.

Example 3.   Factor $3x^2 - 2x - 1$

Solution: $a = 3$, $b = -2$, and $c = -1$. We must find two numbers whose product is a · c, or $3(-1) = -3$, and whose sum is b, -2. The two numbers are -3 and 1.

Rewrite the **bx** term $-2x$ using -3 and 1.

$$3x^2 - 2x - 1 = 3x^2 - 3x + 1x - 1$$

Now factor by grouping.

$$= 3x(x - 1) + 1(x - 1)$$

$$= (3x + 1)(x - 1)$$

Summary:

To Factor Trinomials of the Form $ax^2 + bx + c$,
       $a \neq 1$ Using Trial and Error

1. Write all pairs of factors of the coefficient of the squared term, **a**.

2. Write all pairs of factors of the constant, **c**.

3. Try various combinations of these factors until the correct middle term, **bx**, is found.

Example 4. Factor $3x^2 + 14x - 24$.

Solution: The only factors of 3 are 1 and 3. Therefore, we write

$$3x^2 + 14x - 24 = (3x\quad)(x\quad).$$

The number -24 has both positive and negative factors. Since the last term is -24, we must have one positive factor of -24 and one negative factor.

Possible Factors	Sum of Products of Outer and Inner Terms
$(3x - 1)(x + 24)$	$+71x$
$(3x - 2)(x + 12)$	$+34x$
$(3x - 3)(x + 8)$	$+21x$
$(3x - 4)(x + 6)$	$+14x$ <-correct middle term
$(3x - 6)(x + 4)$	$+ 6x$
$(3x - 8)(x + 3)$	$+ 1x$
$(3x - 12)(x + 2)$	$- 6x$
$(3x - 24)(x + 1)$	$-21x$

Thus $3x^2 + 14x - 24 = (3x - 4)(x + 6)$.

Note:

___

Sometimes a more complicated trinomial can be factored by substituting one variable for another.

___

Example 5. Factor $a^4 + 5a^2 + 6$

Solution: Note that $(a^2)^2 = a^4$.

Let $x = a^2$ and rewrite the problem.

$$a^4 + 5a^2 + 6 = (a^2)^2 + 5a^2 + 6$$

$$= x^2 + 5x + 6$$

Now factor $x^2 + 5x + 6 = (x + 2)(x + 3)$.

Finally, substitute a^2 in place of x to obtain

$$= (a^2 + 2)(a^2 + 3).$$

Thus, $a^4 + 5a^2 + 6 = (a^2 + 2)(a^2 + 3)$.

Exercise Set 6.2

Factor each trinomial completely.

1.) $x^2 + 7x + 12$

2.) $a^2 + 15a + 36$

3.) $b^2 - 6b - 27$

4.) $2y^2 + 10y + 12$

5.) $4x^2 + 28x + 48$

6.) $2x^2 - 11x - 21$

7.) $3x^2 + 8x + 4$

8.) $6x^2 + 19x + 15$

9.) $y^4 + 4y^2 + 4$

10.) $2x^4 - 2x^2 - 24$

Solution to Exercise Set 6.2

1.) $(x + 3)(x + 4)$

2.) $(a + 3)(a + 12)$

3.) $(b - 9)(b + 3)$

4.) $2(y + 2)(y + 3)$

5.) $4(x + 3)(x + 4)$

6.) $(2x + 3)(x - 7)$

7.) $(3x + 2)(x + 2)$

8.) $(2x + 3)(3x + 5)$

9.) $(y^2 + 2)^2$

10.) $(x^2 + 3)(2x^2 - 8)$

Section 6.3 Special Factoring Formulas

Summary:

Difference of Two Squares

$$a^2 - b^2 = (a + b)(a - b)$$

Example 1. Factor each of the following differences of squares using the difference of two squares formula:

a.) $x^2 - 64$

b.) $4x^2 - y^2$

c.) $9x^{10} - 4y^6$

Solution: a.) $x^2 - 64 = (x)^2 - (8)^2$

$$= (x + 8)(x - 8)$$

b.) $4x^2 - y^2 = (2x)^2 - (y)^2$

$$= (2x + y)(2x - y)$$

c.) $9x^{10} - 4y^6 = (3x^5)^2 - (2y^3)^2$

$$= (3x^5 + 2y^3)(3x^5 - 2y^3)$$

Summary:

Perfect Square Trinomials

$$a^2 + 2ab + b^2 = (a + b)^2$$

$$a^2 - 2ab + b^2 = (a - b)^2$$

Example 2. Factor   a.) $x^2 + 12x + 36$

b.) $x^2 - 6x + 9$

Solution: a.) Since the first and last terms are squares, x^2, and 6^2, respectively, this trinomial may be a perfect square trinomial. Since the middle term, 12x, is twice the product of x and 6, the trinomial is a perfect square trinomial and we factor using the formula.

$$a^2 + 2ab + b^2 = (a + b)^2$$

$$x^2 + 12x + 36 = (x + 6)^2$$

b.) Since the first and last terms are squares, x^2 and 3^2, and the middle term is twice the product of 3 and x or 6x, the trinomial is a perfect square trinomial. Since the middle term is -, we factor as follows.

$$x^2 - 6x + 9 = (x - 3)^2$$

Summary:

Sum of Two Cubes
$$a^3 + b^3 = (a + b)(a^2 - ab + b^2)$$

Difference of Two Cubes
$$a^3 - b^3 = (a - b)(a^2 + ab + b^2)$$

Example 3. Factor a.) $x^3 + 8$

b.) $8x^3 - 27$

c.) $64x^6 + 27y^3$

Solution: a.) Write $x^3 + 8$ as the sum of two cubes.

$$x^3 + 8 = (x)^3 + (2)^3$$

$$= (x + 2)(x^2 - x(2) + 2^2)$$

$$= (x + 2)(x^2 - 2x + 4)$$

b.) Since $8x^3$ and 27 have no common factors other than 1, we can factor the expression using the difference of two cubes.

$$8x^3 - 27 = (2x)^3 - (3)^3$$

$$= (2x - 3)[(2x)^2 + 2x(3) + 3^2]$$

$$= (2x - 3)(4x^2 - 6x + 9)$$

c.) Since $64x^6$ and $27y^3$ are perfect cubes of $4x^2$ and $3y$, and they have no common factor other than 1, write the expression as the sum of two cubes.

$$64x^6 + 27y^3$$

$$= (4x^2)^3 + (3y)^3$$

$$= (4x^2 + 3y)[(4x^2)^2 - 4x(3y) + (3y)^2]$$

$$= (4x^2 + 3y)(16x^4 - 12xy + 9y^2)$$

Exercise Set 6.3

Use a special factoring formula to factor each expression.

1.) $x^2 - 49$

2.) $4x^2 - 121$

3.) $144y^6 - 81x^{10}$

4.) $25a^2b^4 - 16a^4b^2$

5.) $x^2 + 18x + 81$

6.) $x^2 - 14x + 49$

7.) $3x^2 - 18x + 27$

8.) $125x^3 - 27$

9.) $64x^3 + 8y^3$

10.) $27x^9 - 64y^6$

Solution to Exercise Set 6.3

1.) $(x + 7)(x - 7)$

2.) $(2x + 11)(2x - 11)$

3.) $9(4y^3 + 3x^5)(4y^3 - 3x^5)$

4.) $(5ab^2 + 4a^2b)(5ab^2 - 4a^2b)$

5.) $(x + 9)^2$

6.) $(x - 7)^2$

7.) $3(x - 3)^2$

8.) $(5x - 3)(25x^2 + 15x + 9)$

9.) $(4x + 2y)(16x^2 - 8xy + 4y^2)$

10.) $(3x^3 - 4y^2)(9x^6 + 12x^3y^2 + 16y^4)$

Section 6.4 A General Review of Factoring

Summary:

To Factor a Polynomial

1. Determine if the polynomial has a greatest common factor other than 1. If so, factor out the GCF from every term in the polynomial.

2. If the polynomial has two terms (or is a binomial), determine if it is a difference of two cubes. If so, factor using the appropriate formula.

3. If the polynomial has three terms (or is a trinomial), determine if it is a perfect square trinomial. If so, factor accordingly. If it is not, then factor the trinomial using the method discussed in Section 6.2.

4. If the polynomial has more than three terms, try factoring by grouping. If that does not work, see if 3 of the terms are the square of a binomial.

5. As a final step, examine your factored polynomial to see if any factors listed have a common factor and can be factored further. If you find a common factor, factor it out at this point.

Example 1.   Factor $5x^4 - 5x^2$

Solution: Begin by factor $5x^2$ as the GCF .

$$5x^4 + 5x^2 = 5x^2(x^2 - 1)$$

Since $x^2 - 1$ is the difference of two squares, apply the appropriate formula.

$$5x^2 (x^2 - 1) = 5x^2 (x + 1)(x - 1)$$

-158-

Example 2.   Factor $5x^7y^3 - 30x^6y^3 + 45x^5y^3$

Solution: Begin by factoring the GCF, $5x^5y^3$, from each term.

$$5x^7y^3 - 30x^6y^3 + 45x^5y^3 = 5x^5y^3(x^2 - 6x + 9)$$

Note that $x^2 - 6x + 9$ is a perfect square trinomial.

$$= 5x^5y^3(x - 3)^2$$

Example 3.   Factor $30x^3 + 36x^2y + 45x^2y + 54xy^2$

Solution: Factor the GCF of $3x$ from each term.

$$30x^3 + 36x^2y + 45x^2y + 54xy^2$$
$$= 3x(10x^2 + 12xy + 15xy + 18y^2)$$

Next factor by grouping.

$$= 3x[2x(5x + 6y) + 3y(5x + 6y)]$$
$$= 3x[(2x + 3y)(5x + 6y)]$$

Exercise Set 6.4

Factor each of the following completely.

1.) $6x^2 - 2x - 20$

2.) $8x^4 + 50x^3 + 12x^2$

3.) $-5x^3 + 5x$

4.) $4x^2 - 8x + 4$

5.) $3x^3y - 3xy^3$

6.) $9x^4 + 3x^3 - 30x^2$

7.) $42x^4y - 14x^3y^2 + 21x^3y^2 - 7x^2y^3$

8.) $8a^3b + 64a^2b + 56a^2b + 448ab$

Solution to Exercise Set 6.4

1.) $2(3x + 5)(x - 2)$

2.) $2x^2(4x + 1)(x + 6)$

3.) $-5x(x + 1)(x - 1)$

4.) $4(x - 1)^2$

5.) $3xy(x + y)(x - y)$

6.) $3x^2(x + 2)(3x - 5)$

7.) $7x^2y(2x + y)(3x - y)$

8.) $8ab(a + 7)(a + 8)$

Section 6.5 Solving Equations Using Factoring

Summary:

Standard Form of a Quadratic Equation

$$ax^2 + bx + c = 0 \qquad a \neq 0$$

where **a**, **b**, and **c** are real numbers.

Zero-Factor Property

For all real numbers **a** and **b**, if $a \cdot b = 0$, then either $a = 0$ or $b = 0$, or both **a** and $b = 0$.

Example 1. Solve the equation $(x - 2)(x + 3) = 0$.

Solution: Since the product of the factors equal zero, use the zero factor property and set each factor to zero.

$$x - 2 = 0 \qquad \text{or} \qquad x + 3 = 0$$

$$x = 2 \qquad \text{or} \qquad x = -3$$

Thus, if **x** is either 2 or -3, the product of the factors is 0.

Check:

$x = 2$	$x = -3$
$(x - 2)(x + 3) = 0$	$(x - 2)(x + 3) = 0$
$(2 - 2)(2 + 3) = 0$	$(-3 - 2)(-3 + 3) = 0$
$0(5) = 0$	$(-5)0 = 0$
True $0 = 0$	True $0 = 0$

Summary:

To Solve an Equation Using Factoring

1. Use the addition property to remove all terms from one side of the equation. This will result in one side of the equation being equal to 0.

2. Combine like terms in the equation and then factor.

3. Set each factor containing a variable equal to zero, solve the equations, and find the solutions.

4. Check the solutions in the original equation.

Example 2.   Solve the equation $3x^2 - 6x = 0$.

Solution: Since all terms are already on the left side of the equation and set equal to zero, factor the left side of the equation.

$$3x^2 - 6x = 0$$

$$3x(x - 2) = 0$$

Now set each factor equal to 0.

$$3x = 0 \qquad \text{or} \qquad x - 2 = 0$$

$$x = 0 \qquad \text{or} \qquad x = 2$$

The numbers 0 and 2 both satisfy the equation.

Example 3. Solve the equation $(2x + 5)(x - 1) = -6x$.

Solution: Begin by multiplying the factor on the left side of the equation.

$$(2x + 5)(x - 1) = -6x$$

$$2x^2 + 3x - 5 = -6x$$

Add 6x to both sides of the equation to get all terms on one side of the equation set equal to zero on the other side of the equation.

$$2x^2 + 9x - 5 = 0$$

Factor the left hand side of the equation.

$$(2x - 1)(x + 5) = 0$$

Set each factor equal to zero and solve.

$$2x - 1 = 0 \qquad \text{or} \qquad x + 5 = 0$$

$$2x = 1 \qquad \text{or} \qquad x = -5$$

$$x = \tfrac{1}{2}$$

The solutions are $x = \tfrac{1}{2}$ or $x = -5$.

Example 4. The area of a rectangle is 84 square centimeters. If the length of the rectangle is 2 cm. less than twice the width of the rectangle, find the deminsions of the rectangle.

Solution: Let x = the width of the rectangle in cm.
Let $2x - 2$ = the length of the rectangle in cm.

$$\text{Area} = (\text{length})(\text{width})$$

$$84 = (2x - 2)(x)$$

$$84 = 2x^2 - 2x$$

$$0 = 2x^2 - 2x - 84$$

$$0 = x^2 - x - 42$$

$$0 = (x - 7)(x + 6)$$

Either $x - 7 = 0$ or $x + 6 = 0$

$$x = 7 \qquad\qquad x = -6$$

Since the dimensions of a geometric figure cannot be negative, $x = -6$ is eliminated as an answer. Therefore $x = 7$ and $2x - 2 = 12$.

Exercise Set 6.5

Solve each equation.

1.) $2x^2 - 8x = 0$ 2.) $4x^2 - 32x = 0$

3.) $(x + 5)(x - 6) = 0$ 4.) $4x^2 - 64 = 0$

5.) $8x^2 - 16x = -8$ 6.) $x^2 = 14x - 49$

7.) $3x^2 - 18x = -21$ 8.) $(3x + 5)(x - 2) = -8x$

9.) $(2x + 3)(x + 4) = 16x$ 10.) $(2x + 5)(x + 1) = -4x$

11.) The product of two consecutive odd integers is 195.
Find the two integers.

12.) The area of a rectangle is 18 square meters. If the
length of the rectangle is one meter more than four
times the width of the rectangle, what are the
dimensions of the rectangle?

Solution to Exercise Set 6.5

1.) $x = 0$ or $x = 4$

2.) $x = 0$ or $x = 8$

3.) $x = -5$ or $x = 6$

4.) $x = 4$ or $x = -4$

5.) $x = 1$ or $x = 1$

6.) $x = 7$ or $x = 7$

7.) $x = 7$ or $x = -1$

8.) $x = 1$ or $x = -10/3$

9.) $x = 6$ or $x = -1$

10.) $x = \frac{1}{2}$ or $x = -5$

11.) 13, 15

12.) width $= 2$m. , length 9 m.

Practice Test   Chapter 6

Factor completely.

1.) $5x^2 - 60x$

2.) $3x^2y^3 - 6x^2y^2$

3.) $3x^2 - 12x - 2x + 8$

4.) $4x^4y^3 - 12x^2y^4 + 8x^5y^4$

5.) $4x(x - 1) + 12(x - 1)$

6.) $4x^2 - 8x + 4$

7.) $x^2 + 17x + 72$

8.) $2x^2 - 2y^2$

9.) $x^3 - 125$

10.) $8x^6 + 27y^9$

11.) $2x^2 - xy - y^2$

12.) $6x^2 + 17x + 12$

13.) $20x^2 + 19x + 3$

14.) $2x^2 + x - 15$

15.) $9x^3 + 30x^2 - 24x$

Solve the equation.

16.) $(2x + 5)(x - 4) = 0$

17.) $3(x - 2)(x - 4) = 0$

18.) $x^2 + 5x = +36$

19.) $x^3 + 9x^2 = -14x$

20.) The area of a rectangle is 60 square feet. Find the dimensions of the rectangle if the length of the rectangle is 2 feet less than twice the width of the rectangle.

Solution to Practice Test   Chapter 6

1.) $5x(x - 12)$

2.) $3x^2y^2(y - 2)$

3.) $(3x - 2)(x - 4)$

4.) $4x^2y^3(x^2 - 3y + 2x^3y)$

5.) $4(x + 3)(x - 1)$

6.) $4(x - 1)^2$

7.) $(x + 8)(x + 9)$

8.) $2(x + y)(x - y)$

9.) $(x - 5)(x^2 + 5x + 25)$

10.) $(2x^2 + 3y^3)(4x^4 - 6x^2y^3 + 9y^6)$

11.) $(2x + y)(x - y)$

12.) $(2x + 3)(3x + 4)$

13.) $(4x + 3)(5x + 1)$

14.) $(2x - 5)(x + 3)$

15.) $3x(3x - 2)(x + 4)$

16.) $x = -2\frac{1}{2}$ or $x = 4$

17.) $x = 2$ or $x = 4$

18.) $x = -9$ or $x = 4$

19.) $x = 0$ or $x = -2$ or $x = -7$

20.) width = 6, length = 10

Chapter 7 Rational Expressions and Equations

Section 7.1 Reducing Rational Expressions

Summary:

A rational expression (also called a ~~algebraic fraction~~) is an algebraic expression of the form **p/q**, where **p** and **q** are polynomials and **p ≠ 0**. When discussing rational expressions, the **domain** will be the set of values that can be used to replace the variable. The domain will be all real numbers except any real number that would make the denominator of the rational expression equal to 0.

Example 1. Find the domain of:

$$\text{a.) } \frac{3x - 5}{2x - 8} \qquad\qquad \text{b.) } \frac{4 + 6x}{x^2 - 16x + 48}$$

Solution: We must determine the values that make the denominator equal to zero.

a.) Set $2x - 8 = 0$ and solve for x.

$$2x - 8 = 0$$

$$2x = 8$$

$$x = 4$$

Domain: $\{x \mid x \neq 4\}$

b.) Set $x^2 - 16x + 48 = 0$ and solve for x.

$$x^2 - 16x + 48 = 0$$

$$(x - 4)(x - 12) = 0$$

$$x - 4 = 0 \quad \text{or} \quad x - 12 = 0$$

$$x = 4 \quad \text{or} \quad x = 12$$

Domain: $\{x \mid x \neq 4, x \neq 12\}$

-168-

Summary:

An algebraic fraction is **reduced to its lowest terms** when the numerator and denominator have no common factors other than 1.

To Reduce Rational Expressions

1. Factor both numerator and denominator as completely as possible.

2. Divide both the numerator and the denominator by any common factors.

Example 2.   Reduce each expression to its lowest terms.

a.) $\dfrac{x^2 + 9x + 14}{x + 7}$

b.) $\dfrac{x^2 - 5x - 6}{42 - 7x}$

Solution: a.) Factor the numerator, then divide out the common factor.

$$\frac{x^2 + 9x + 14}{x + 7} = \frac{(x + 2)(x + 7)}{(x + 7)} = x + 2$$

The expression reduces to $x + 2$.

b.) Factor both the numerator and denominator, then divide out any common factors.

$$\frac{x^2 - 5x - 6}{42 - 7x} = \frac{(x - 6)(x + 1)}{7(6 - x)}$$

$$= \frac{(x - 6)(x + 1)}{7(-1)(x - 6)} \quad \frac{-x + 1}{-7}$$

$$= \frac{x + 1}{-7}$$

Exercise Set 7.1

Determine the domain of the following.

$x^2 + 9x + 14$ *(handwritten)*

1.) $\dfrac{7}{x - 8}$ = $\begin{aligned}x - 8 &= 0 \quad \{x \mid x \neq 8\}\\ -8 + 8 &= 0 \\ x &= 8\end{aligned}$ *(handwritten)*

2.) $\dfrac{12}{x^2 + 9x + 14}$ =

3.) $\dfrac{-7x}{8x + 3}$

4.) $\dfrac{8 - 2x}{x^2 - 9}$

5.) $\dfrac{3x^2 + 8x + 5}{(x + 4)(x - 7)}$

Reduce each expression to lowest terms.

6.) $\dfrac{x^2 - 4x}{x}$

7.) $\dfrac{8x - 4}{2x - 1}$

8.) $\dfrac{4x + 8xy}{2x}$

9.) $\dfrac{x^2 - 49}{7 - x}$

10.) $\dfrac{x^2 + 11x + 30}{x^2 - 25}$

Solution to Exercise Set 7.1

1.) $\{x \mid x \neq 8\}$

2.) $\{x \mid x \neq -2, x \neq -7\}$

3.) $\{x \mid x \neq 3/8\}$

4.) $\{x \mid x \neq -3, x \neq 3\}$

5.) $\{x \mid x \neq -4, x \neq 7\}$

6.) $x - 4$

7.) 4

8.) $2 + 4y$

9.) $-(x + 7)$

10.) $\dfrac{x + 6}{x + 5}$

-170-

Section 7.2 Multiplication and Division of Rational Expressions

Summary:

To Multiply Rational Expressions

1. Factor all numerators and denominators as far as possible.

2. Divide out or cancel the common factors.

3. Multiply numerators together and multiply denominators together.

4. Reduce the answer when possible.

Example 1. Multiply $\dfrac{6a^2}{16b^3} \cdot \dfrac{8b^2}{21a} = \dfrac{a}{7b}$

Solution:

$$\dfrac{6a^2}{16b^3} \cdot \dfrac{8b^2}{21a} = \dfrac{a}{7b}$$

Example 2. Multiply $\dfrac{x - 3}{3x} \cdot \dfrac{3x^2 - 9x}{x^2 - 9} =$

Solution: $\dfrac{x - 3}{3x} \cdot \dfrac{3x^2 - 9x}{x^2 - 9} = \dfrac{x - 3}{3x} \cdot \dfrac{3x(x - 3)}{(x - 3)(x + 3)} = \dfrac{x - 3}{x + 3}$

Example 3.   Multiply $\dfrac{x^2 + 5x + 6}{x^2 + 6x + 9} \cdot \dfrac{x - 5x + 6}{2 - x}$

Solution: $\dfrac{x^2 + 5x + 6}{x^2 + 6x + 9} \cdot \dfrac{x - 5x + 6}{2 - x}$

$= \dfrac{(x + 2)(x + 3)}{(x + 3)(x + 3)} \cdot \dfrac{(x - 2)(x - 3)}{2 - x}$

$= \dfrac{(x + 2)(x + 3)}{(x + 3)(x + 3)} \cdot \dfrac{(x - 2)(x - 3)}{-1(x - 2)}$

$= \dfrac{(x + 2)(x - 3)}{-1(x + 3)} = \dfrac{(x + 2)(x - 3)}{-x - 3}$

Summary:

To Divide Rational Expressions

Invert the divisor (the second or bottom fraction) and then multiply the resulting rational expressions.

Example 4.   Divide $\dfrac{60x^{12}}{24y^2} \div \dfrac{15x^4}{48y^5}$

Solution:

$\dfrac{60x^{12}}{24y^2} \div \dfrac{15x^4}{48y^5} = \dfrac{\cancel{60}x^{12}}{\cancel{24}y^2} \cdot \dfrac{\cancel{48}y^5}{\cancel{15}x^4} = 8x^8y^3$

Example 5.   Divide $\dfrac{x^2 + 6x + 9}{x + 2} \div \dfrac{x + 3}{x + 2}$

Solution: $\dfrac{x^2 + 6x + 9}{x + 2} \div \dfrac{x + 3}{x + 2} = \dfrac{(x + 3)(x + 3)}{x + 2} \cdot \dfrac{x + 2}{x + 3}$

$= x + 3$

Example 6.   Divide $\dfrac{2x^2 + 5x + 3}{x + 2} \div \dfrac{2x^2 + 7x + 6}{2x + 3}$

Solution: $\dfrac{2x^2 + 5x + 3}{x + 2} \div \dfrac{2x^2 + 7x + 6}{2x + 4}$

$= \dfrac{2x^2 + 5x + 3}{x + 2} \cdot \dfrac{2x + 4}{2x^2 + 7x + 6}$

$= \dfrac{(2x + 3)(x + 1)}{x + 2} \cdot \dfrac{2(x + 2)}{(2x + 3)(x + 2)}$

$= \dfrac{x + 1}{x + 2}$

Exercise Set 7.2

Multiply as indicated.

1.) $\dfrac{2x}{3y} \cdot \dfrac{6y^3}{5x} = \dfrac{4y^{2 \cdot 3}}{5x}$

2.) $\dfrac{20x^2}{3y^2} \cdot \dfrac{24y}{5x} = \dfrac{32x^2}{y}$

3.) $\dfrac{20a^2b^3}{6ab^2} \cdot \dfrac{5ab}{10a^2b^2}$

4.) $\dfrac{x + 2}{2x} \cdot \dfrac{2x^2 + 4x}{x^2 - 4}$

5.) $\dfrac{x + 1}{4x} \cdot \dfrac{8x}{x^2 + 2x + 1}$

6.) $\dfrac{x + 3}{5x} \cdot \dfrac{5x + 10}{x^2 + 5x + 6}$

7.) $\dfrac{x^2 + 4x + 4}{x + 3} \cdot \dfrac{x^2 + 5x + 6}{x^2 + 6x + 8}$

8.) $\dfrac{x + 5}{x^2 + 6x + 9} \cdot \dfrac{x^2 - 9}{x^2 + 2x - 15}$

9.) $\dfrac{x + 4}{x^2 + 9x + 14} \cdot \dfrac{x + 7}{x^2 + 11x + 28}$

Divide as indicated.

10.) $\dfrac{12x^2}{5y} \div \dfrac{36x}{25y^3}$

11.) $\dfrac{18x^3y^2}{5xy} \div \dfrac{24x^2y^2}{20x^3y}$

12.) $\dfrac{30x^4y^3}{4x^2y} \div \dfrac{12x^2}{5y}$

13.) $\dfrac{3x}{x^2 - 4} \div \dfrac{8x}{x + 2}$

14.) $\dfrac{12y^3}{x^2 + 8x + 16} \div \dfrac{3y}{x^2 - 16}$

15.) $\dfrac{6x^2y^3}{x + 3} \div \dfrac{8x^3y}{x^2 - 4x - 21}$

16.) $\dfrac{x^2 + 10x + 21}{x + 4} \div \dfrac{x^2 - 49}{x^2 + x - 12}$

17.) $\dfrac{x^2 - 9}{x^2 + 12x + 36} \div \dfrac{x^2 + 5x + 6}{x^2 + 8x + 12}$

18.) $\dfrac{3x^2 - x - 2}{x + 1} \div \dfrac{1 - x}{3x^2 + 5x + 2}$

Solution to Exercise Set 7.2

1.) $\dfrac{4y^2}{5}$ 2.) $\dfrac{32x}{y}$ 3.) $\dfrac{5}{3}$ 4.) $\dfrac{x+2}{x-2}$

5.) $\dfrac{2}{x+1}$ 6.) $\dfrac{1}{x}$ 7.) $\dfrac{(x+2)^2}{x+4}$ 8.) $\dfrac{1}{x+3}$

9.) $\dfrac{1}{(x+2)(x+7)}$ 10.) $\dfrac{5xy^2}{3}$

11.) $3x^3$ 12.) $75y^3$

13.) $\dfrac{3}{8(x-2)}$ 14.) $\dfrac{4y^2(x-4)}{x+4}$

15.) $\dfrac{3y(x-7)}{4x}$ 16.) $\dfrac{(x+3)(x-3)}{x-7}$

17.) $\dfrac{x-3}{x+6}$ 18.) $-(3x+2)^2$

Section 7.3 Addition and Subtraction of Rational Expressions

Summary:

To Add or Subtract Expressions with a Common Denominator

1. Add or subtract the numerators.

2. Place the sum or difference of the numerators found in part 1 over the common denominator.

3. Reduce the fraction if possible.

Example 1. Add $\dfrac{3x + 4}{2x + 5} + \dfrac{6x - 8}{2x + 5}$

Solution: $\dfrac{3x + 4}{2x + 5} + \dfrac{6x - 8}{2x + 5} = \dfrac{3x + 4 + (6x - 8)}{2x + 5}$

$$= \dfrac{9x - 4}{2x + 5}$$

Example 2. Subtract $\dfrac{4x - 6}{x + 5} - \dfrac{6x + 7}{x + 5}$

Solution: When subtracting rational expressions, be sure to subtract the entire numerator of the fraction being subtracted.

$$\dfrac{4x - 6}{x + 5} - \dfrac{6x + 7}{x + 5} = \dfrac{4x - 6 - (6x + 7)}{x + 5}$$

$$= \dfrac{4x - 6 - 6x - 7}{x + 5}$$

$$= \dfrac{-2x - 13}{x + 5}$$

Note that the sign of each term (not just the first term) in the numerator of the fraction being subtracted must change.

Summary:

To Find the Least Common Denominator of Rational Expressions (LCD)

1. Factor each demonimator completely. Factors in any given denominator that occur more than once should be expressed as powers [therefore, $(x + 5)(x + 5)$ should be expressed as $(x + 5)^2$].

2. List all different factors (other than 1) that appear in any of the denominators. When the same factor appears in more than one denominator, write the factor with the **highest** power that appears.

3. The least common denominator is the product of all the factors found in step 2.

Example 3. Find the LCD.

$$\frac{2}{3x^2} - \frac{7}{2x^3}$$

Solution: The factors that appear in the denominator are
2, 3, and x. List each factor with its highest
power.

The LCM is the product of these factors.

LCM or LCD = $2 \cdot 3 \cdot x^3 = 6x^3$.

Example 4. Find the LCD.

a.) $\frac{2}{14x^2y} - \frac{8}{49xy^3}$

b.) $\frac{2}{3x + 6} + \frac{4}{x^2 + 4x + 4}$

Solution: a.) The LCD of 14 and 49 is 98.
The variable factors are **x** and **y**.

LCD = $98x^2y^3$

b.) Factor 3x + 6 and x² + 4x + 4

3x + 6 = 3(x + 2)

x² + 4x + 4 = (x + 2)(x + 2)

The factors that appear are 3 and (x + 2).

LCD = 3(x + 2)²

Summary:

To Add or Subtract Two Rational Expressions
with Unlike Denominators

1. Determine the LCD.
2. Rewrite each fraction as an equivalent fraction with the LCD. This is done by multiplying both the numerator and denominator of each fraction by any factors needed to obtain the LCD.
3. Leave the denominator in factored form but multiply out the numerator.
4. Add or subtract the numerators while maintaining the LCD.
5. When possible, factor the remaining numerator and reduce fractions.

Example 5.   Add $\dfrac{3}{2x^3y} + \dfrac{4}{3xy^2}$

Solution: The **LCD** is $6x^3y^2$. We must write each fraction with the denominator $6x^3y^2$.

To do this, multiply the fraction on the left by $3y/3y$ and the fraction on the right by $2x^2/2x^2$.

$$\frac{3y}{3y} \cdot \frac{3}{2x^3y} + \frac{4}{3xy^2} \cdot \frac{2x^2}{2x^2} = \frac{9y}{6x^3y^2} + \frac{8x^2}{6x^3y^2} = \frac{9y + 8x^2}{6x^3y^2}$$

Example 6.   Subtract $\dfrac{5}{x-2} - \dfrac{2}{x}$

Solution: Write each fraction with LCD $x(x-2)$. To do this, multiply the fraction on the left by x/x and the fraction on the right by $(x-2)/(x-2)$.

$$\frac{x}{x} \cdot \frac{5}{x-2} + \frac{2}{x} \cdot \frac{(x-2)}{(x-2)} = \frac{5x}{x(x-2)} + \frac{2(x-2)}{x(x-2)}$$

$$= \frac{5x + 2(x-2)}{x(x-2)}$$

$$= \frac{5x + 2x - 4}{x(x-2)}$$

$$= \frac{7x - 4}{x(x-2)}$$

Example 7. Add $\dfrac{2x + 3}{x^2 + 5x + 6} + \dfrac{3x + 1}{x^2 - x - 6}$

Solution: Factor the denominators first.

$$\frac{2x + 3}{(x + 2)(x + 3)} + \frac{3x + 1}{(x + 2)(x - 3)}$$

The LCD is $(x + 2)(x + 3)(x - 3)$

$$\frac{2x + 3}{(x + 2)(x + 3)} + \frac{3x + 1}{(x + 2)(x - 3)}$$

$$= \frac{x - 3}{x - 3} \cdot \frac{2x + 3}{(x + 2)(x + 3)} + \frac{3x + 1}{(x + 2)(x - 3)} \cdot \frac{x + 3}{x + 3}$$

$$= \frac{(x - 3)(2x + 3)}{(x + 2)(x + 3)(x - 3)} + \frac{(3x + 1)(x + 3)}{(x + 2)(x + 3)(x - 3)}$$

$$= \frac{2x^2 - 3x - 9 + (3x^2 + 10x + 3)}{(x + 2)(x + 3)(x - 3)}$$

$$= \frac{2x^2 - 3x - 9 + 3x^2 + 10x + 3}{(x + 2)(x + 3)(x - 3)}$$

$$= \frac{5x^2 + 7x - 6}{(x + 2)(x + 3)(x - 3)}$$

$$= \frac{(5x - 3)(x + 2)}{(x + 2)(x + 3)(x - 3)}$$

$$= \frac{5x - 3}{(x + 3)(x - 3)}$$

Exercise Set 7.3

Add or subtract as indicated.

1.) $\dfrac{8x + 7}{x^2} + \dfrac{2x - 9}{x^2}$

2.) $\dfrac{3x - 5}{2x^3} - \dfrac{2x - 5}{2x^3}$

3.) $\dfrac{2}{2x^2y} + \dfrac{3}{2x^2y}$

4.) $\dfrac{x + 2}{3x^3y} - \dfrac{x - 2}{3x^3y}$

5.) $\dfrac{6x - 2}{x + 5} - \dfrac{4x + 8}{x + 5}$

Find the least common denominator.

6.) $\dfrac{4}{x + 3} + \dfrac{7}{x + 2}$

7.) $\dfrac{2x}{5x^2} - \dfrac{3x}{3x^3}$

8.) $\dfrac{7x}{16x^2y^3} + \dfrac{4x}{20xy^6}$

9.) $\dfrac{2}{3x + 6} - \dfrac{7}{x^2 - 9}$

10.) $\dfrac{x - 2}{5x^2 - 18x - 8} - \dfrac{9}{x^2 - 8x - 16}$

Add or subtract as indicated. (Be sure to reduce your answer to the lowest terms.)

11.) $\dfrac{2}{5x} + \dfrac{7}{x}$

12.) $\dfrac{5}{3x^3} - \dfrac{2}{4x}$

13.) $\dfrac{5}{x + 2} - \dfrac{3}{x - 1}$

14.) $\dfrac{7}{3x + 9} - \dfrac{12}{x^2 - 9}$

15.) $\dfrac{x - 2}{5x^2 - 18x - 8} - \dfrac{9}{x^2 - 8x + 16}$

Solution to Exercise Set 7.3

1.) $\dfrac{10x - 2}{x^2}$

2.) $\dfrac{1}{2x^2}$

3.) $\dfrac{5}{2x^2 y}$

4.) $\dfrac{4}{3x^3 y}$

5.) 2

6.) $(x + 2)(x + 3)$

7.) $15x^3$

8.) $80x^2 y^6$

9.) $3(x + 2)(x + 3)(x - 3)$

10.) $(5x + 2)(x - 4)^2$

11.) $\dfrac{37}{5x}$

12.) $\dfrac{10 - 3x^2}{6x^3}$

13.) $\dfrac{2x - 11}{(x + 2)(x - 1)}$

14.) $\dfrac{7x - 57}{3(x + 3)(x - 3)}$

15.) $\dfrac{x^2 - 51x - 10}{(5x + 2)(x - 4)^2}$

Section 7.4 Complex Fractions

Summary:

A **complex fraction** is one that has a fractional expression in its numerator or its denominator or both its numerator and denominator.

numerator of
complex fraction

secondary fraction

$$\frac{\dfrac{a + b}{a}}{\dfrac{a - b}{b}}$$

main fraction line

secondary fraction

demonimator of
complex fraction

To Simplify a Complex Fraction

(by multiplying by a common denominator)

1. Find the least common denominator of each of the two secondary fractions.

2. Next, find the **LCD** of the complex fraction. The **LCD** of the complex fraction will be the **LCD** of the two expressions found in step 1.

3. Multiply both secondary fractions by the **LCD** of the complex fraction found in step 2.

4. Simplify when possible.

Example 1. Simplify $\dfrac{\dfrac{1}{3} + \dfrac{3}{5}}{\dfrac{2}{3} + \dfrac{1}{6}}$

Solution: The LCD of the numerator of the complex fraction is 15 and the LCD of the denominator is 6. The LCD of the complex fraction is the LCD of 15 and 6, which is 30. Multiply both secondary fractions by 30.

$$\frac{30\left(\dfrac{1}{3} + \dfrac{3}{5}\right)}{30\left(\dfrac{2}{3} + \dfrac{1}{6}\right)} = \frac{30\left(\dfrac{1}{3}\right) + 30\left(\dfrac{3}{5}\right)}{30\left(\dfrac{2}{3}\right) + 30\left(\dfrac{1}{6}\right)}$$

Simplifying you get:

$$= \frac{10 + 18}{20 + 5}$$

$$= \frac{28}{25}$$

Example 2. Simplify $\dfrac{\dfrac{3}{2x} - \dfrac{5}{3x^2}}{\dfrac{6}{x} - \dfrac{8}{4x^3}}$

Solution: The LCD of the numerator of the complex fraction is $6x^2$ and the LCD of the denominator is $4x^3$.

The LCD of the complex fraction is the LCD of $6x^2$ and $4x^3$, which is $12x^3$.

Multiply both secondary fractions by $12x^3$.

$$\frac{12x^3\left(\dfrac{3}{2x} - \dfrac{5}{3x^2}\right)}{12x^3\left(\dfrac{6}{x} - \dfrac{8}{4x^3}\right)} = \frac{12x^3\left(\dfrac{3}{2x}\right) - 12x^3\left(\dfrac{5}{3x^2}\right)}{12x^3\left(\dfrac{6}{x}\right) - 12x^3\left(\dfrac{8}{4x^3}\right)}$$

-183-

Simplifying you get:

$$= \frac{18x^2 - 20x}{72x^2 - 24}$$

$$= \frac{2x(9x - 10)}{24(3x^2 - 1)}$$

$$= \frac{x(9x - 10)}{12(3x^2 - 1)}$$

Summary:

___

To Simplify a Complex Fraction
(by simplifying numerator and denominator)

Complex fractions can also be simplified as follows:

1. Add or subtract each secondary fraction as indicated.

2. Invert and multiply the denominator of the complex fraction by the numerator of the complex fraction.

3. Simplify when possible.

___

Example 3. Simplify

$$\frac{\dfrac{3}{2x} - \dfrac{5}{3x^2}}{\dfrac{6}{x} - \dfrac{8}{4x^3}}$$

Solution: Subtract the fractions in the numerator and the subtractions in the denominator.

$$\frac{\dfrac{3}{2x} - \dfrac{5}{3x^2}}{\dfrac{6}{x} - \dfrac{8}{4x^3}} = \frac{\dfrac{3x}{3x} \cdot \dfrac{3}{2x} - \dfrac{5}{3x^2} \cdot \dfrac{2}{2}}{\dfrac{4x^2}{4x^2} \cdot \dfrac{6}{x} - \dfrac{8}{4x^3}}$$

-184-

$$= \dfrac{\dfrac{9x}{6x^2} - \dfrac{10}{6x^2}}{\dfrac{24x^2}{4x^3} - \dfrac{8}{4x^3}}$$

$$= \dfrac{\dfrac{9x - 10}{6x^2}}{\dfrac{24x^2 - 8}{4x^3}}$$

Invert the denominator of the complex fraction and it by the numerator.

$$= \dfrac{9x - 10}{6x^2} \cdot \dfrac{4x^3}{24x^2 - 8}$$

$$= \dfrac{2x(9x - 10)}{3(24x^2 - 8)}$$

$$= \dfrac{2x(9x - 10)}{3(8)(3x^2 - 1)}$$

$$= \dfrac{x(9x - 10)}{12(3x^2 - 1)}$$

Exercise Set 7.4

Simplify.

1.) $\dfrac{\dfrac{1}{4} + \dfrac{2}{3}}{\dfrac{2}{3} - \dfrac{1}{4}}$

2.) $\dfrac{\dfrac{3}{4} + \dfrac{1}{2}}{\dfrac{4}{5} - \dfrac{1}{2}}$

3.) $\dfrac{1 + \dfrac{2}{3}}{2 - \dfrac{1}{3}}$

4.) $\dfrac{\dfrac{2x^3y^2}{30xy}}{\dfrac{5x^3y^6}{4^2 y^2}}$

5.)
$$\dfrac{\dfrac{8xy^2}{3x^3z}}{\dfrac{3x^3y^3}{4yz^2}}$$

6.)
$$\dfrac{\dfrac{2}{5x} + \dfrac{6}{x}}{\dfrac{1}{3x^2} + \dfrac{2}{x}}$$

7.)
$$\dfrac{\dfrac{1}{a^3} + \dfrac{1}{3a}}{\dfrac{1}{6a} + \dfrac{1}{a^2}}$$

8.)
$$\dfrac{\dfrac{1}{2ab} + \dfrac{3}{a^2b^3}}{\dfrac{6}{3ab} + \dfrac{4}{a^2b^2}}$$

9.)
$$\dfrac{\dfrac{12x + 3}{16x^2}}{\dfrac{4x + -1}{12x^3}}$$

10.)
$$\dfrac{\dfrac{x}{4} - \dfrac{3}{x}}{2 + \dfrac{1}{x^2}}$$

Solution to Exercise Set 7.4

1.) 11/5

2.) 25/6

3.) 1

4.) $\dfrac{4x^2}{15y^3}$

5.) $\dfrac{32z}{9x^5}$

6.) $\dfrac{96x}{5 + 30x}$

7.) $\dfrac{2a^2 + 6}{a^2 + 6a}$

8.) $\dfrac{ab + 6}{4b(ab + 2)}$

9.) $\dfrac{9x}{4}$

10.) $\dfrac{x(x^2 - 12)}{4(2x^2 + 1)}$

**Section 7.5 Solving Equations Containing Rational
            Expressions**

Summary:

_____

To Solve Equations Containing Fractions

1. Determine the LCD of all fractions in the equation.

2. Multiply **both** sides of the equation by the LCD.
    This will result in every term in the equation being
    multiplied by the LCD.

3. Remove any parentheses and combine like terms on each
    side of the equation.

4. Solve the equation using the properties discussed in
    earlier sections.

5. Check the solution in the original equation.

_____

Example 1.   Solve the equation.

$$\frac{x}{2} + 2x = 15$$

Solution: $2\left(\frac{x}{2} + 2x\right) = (15)2$ Multiply both sides of
                                      the equation by the
                                      LCD, 2.

$$2\left(\frac{x}{2}\right) + 2(2x) = (15)2$$

$$x + 4x = 30$$

$$5x = 30$$

$$x = 6$$

Check: $\frac{x}{2} + 2x = 15$

$$\frac{6}{2} + 2(6) = 15$$

$$3 + 12 = 15$$

$$15 = 15 \qquad \text{True}$$

Note: Whenever a variable appears in any denominator you must check your proposed answer in the original equation. When checking if a proposed answer makes any denominator equal to zero, that value is not a solution to the equation. Such values are called **extraneous roots** or **extraneous solutions**. An extraneous root is a number obtained when solving an equation that is not a solution to the original equation.

Example 2. $\dfrac{3}{x} + \dfrac{7}{2x} = \dfrac{26}{x^2}$

Solution: Multiply both sides of the equation by the LCD, $2x^2$.

$$2x^2\left(\dfrac{3}{x} + \dfrac{7}{2x}\right) = \left(\dfrac{26}{x^2}\right) \cdot 2x^2$$

$$6x + 7x = 52$$

$$13x = 52$$

$$x = 4$$

Check: $\dfrac{3}{x} + \dfrac{7}{2x} = \dfrac{26}{x^2}$

$$\dfrac{3}{4} + \dfrac{7}{8} = \dfrac{26}{16}$$

$$\dfrac{6}{8} + \dfrac{7}{8} = \dfrac{13}{8}$$

$$\dfrac{13}{8} = \dfrac{13}{8} \quad \text{True}$$

Summary:

Cross-Multiplication

$$\text{If } \dfrac{a}{b} = \dfrac{c}{d} \text{ then } ad = bc, \ b \neq 0, \ d \neq 0$$

Example 3.   Solve the following proportion using cross-multiplication.

$$\frac{5}{x + 2} = \frac{3}{x - 7}$$

Solution: $5(x - 7) = 3(x + 2)$

$5x - 35 = 3x + 6$

$2x - 35 = 6$

$2x = 41$

$x = 20.5$

Example 4.   Solve the equation.

$$\frac{x + 2}{2x} + \frac{1}{x + 1} = \frac{x + 3}{2x}$$

Solution: $\dfrac{x + 2}{2x} + \dfrac{1}{x + 1} = \dfrac{x + 3}{2x}$

Multiply both sides of the equation by the LCD, $2x(x + 1)$.

$$2x(x + 1)\left[\frac{x + 2}{2x} + \frac{1}{x + 1}\right] = \left[\frac{x + 3}{2x}\right] \cdot 2x(x + 1)$$

$$2x(x + 1) \cdot \left(\frac{x + 2}{2x}\right) + 2x(x + 1) \cdot \left(\frac{1}{x + 1}\right) = \left[\frac{x + 3}{2x}\right] \cdot 2x(x + 1)$$

$$(x + 1)(x + 2) + 2x = (x + 3)(x + 1)$$

$$x^2 + 3x + 2 + 2x = x^2 + 4x + 3$$

$$x^2 + 5x + 2 = x^2 + 4x + 3$$

$$5x + 2 = 4x + 3$$

$$x + 2 = 3$$

$$x = 1$$

Exercise Set 7.5

Solve each equation and check your solution.

1.) $\dfrac{3}{5} = \dfrac{x}{20}$

2.) $\dfrac{4}{13} = \dfrac{x}{39}$

3.) $\dfrac{x + 2}{5} = \dfrac{3x}{10}$

4.) $\dfrac{5x - 1}{9} = \dfrac{70}{15x}$

5.) $\dfrac{x - 1}{6} = \dfrac{3x + 2}{2}$

6.) $\dfrac{x + 7}{x + 3} = \dfrac{4}{x + 3}$

7.) $\dfrac{1}{x + 2} + \dfrac{1}{x + 3} = \dfrac{15}{56}$

8.) $\dfrac{x}{4} + \dfrac{x}{2x} = \dfrac{x + 2}{2x}$

9.) $\dfrac{x - 4}{x + 2} = \dfrac{1}{x - 2}$

10.) $\dfrac{x + 7}{x - 2} = \dfrac{x + 3}{x + 4}$

Solution to Exercise Set 7.5

1.) x = 12   2.) x = 12

3.) x = 4   4.) x = 14/9

5.) x = -7/8   6.) No solution

7.) x = 5   8.) x = -2 or x = 2

9.) x = 1 or x = 6   10.) x = -3.4

Section 7.6 Applications of Rational Equations

Summary:

Work problems often involve equations containing fractions.
Generally, work problems are based on the fact that the work
done by person 1 (or machine 1) plus the work done by person
2 (or machine 2) is equal to the total amount of work done
by both people (or both machines).

$$\frac{\text{time together}}{\text{time of 1st person alone}} + \frac{\text{time together}}{\text{time of 2nd person alone}} = 1$$

or

fractional part of 1st person

+ fractional part of 2nd person = 1

Example 1.   Ken can wash and wax Mr. Sobon's van in 3 hours
             and Shawn can wash and wax the same van in 5
             hours.   How long will it take Ken and Shawn to
             wash and wax the van working together?

Solution: Let x = time, in hours, for both boys together to
             wash and wax Mr. Sobon's van.

             Then x/3 is the amount of the van that Ken washes
             and waxes, and x/5 is the amount of the van that
             Shawn washes and waxes.

$$\frac{x}{3} + \frac{x}{5} = 1$$

-191-

Multiply both sides by the LCD, 15, then solve for **x**.

$$15 \left(\frac{x}{3} + \frac{x}{5} \right) = (1) \cdot 15$$

$$5x + 3x = 15$$

$$8x = 15$$

$$x = 1\frac{7}{8}$$

Therefore, working together, the boys can wash and wax the van in 1 7/8 hours.

Some other rational number application problems involve finding a given number.

Let us look at an example of that kind of a problem.

Example 2. What number multiplied by the numerator and added to the denominator of the fraction 2/3 makes the resulting number equal to 1.

Solution: Let x = the unknown number.

$$\frac{2x}{3 + x} = 1$$

First cross-multiply, then solve for **x**.

$$2x = 3 + x$$

$$x = 3$$

The number is 3.

Check: $$\frac{2x}{3 + x} = \frac{2(3)}{3 + 3}$$

$$= \frac{6}{6}$$

$$= 1$$

Motion problems involve forms of the distance formula such as:

$$\text{distance} = \text{rate} \cdot \text{time}$$

or

$$\text{time} = \frac{\text{distance}}{\text{rate}}$$

Example 3. Frank and John paddle their canoe on the Genesee River at the rate of 4 m.p.h. upstream against the current and at 7 m.p.h. downstream with the current. If the upstream paddling takes one hour more than the downstream paddling, how far did they travel upstream?

Solution: The assumption is that John and Frank traveled the same distance upstream as downstream.

Let x = the distance traveled in miles upstream.

	d	r	t
Upstream	x	4	$\frac{x}{4}$
Downstream	x	7	$\frac{x}{7}$

$$\frac{x}{4} - 1 = \frac{x}{7}$$

Multiply both sides of the equation by the LCD of 28, then solve for **x**.

$$28 \left[\frac{x}{4} - 1 \right] = \left[\frac{x}{7} \right] 28$$

$$7x - 28 = 4x$$

$$3x - 28 = 0$$

$$3x = 28$$

$$x = 28/3 \text{ miles}$$

Example 4.   Tom Ruggs can paddle his kayak 5 miles upstream
             against a current in the same time it takes to
             paddle 9 miles downstream with the current. If
             the current is 3 miles per hour, find the speed
             of Tom Ruggs paddling the kajak in still water.

Solution: Let x = speed of Tom Ruggs paddling the kayak
                      in still water.

Kayak	d	r	t
With current	9	x + 3	$\dfrac{9}{x + 3}$
Against current	5	x - 3	$\dfrac{5}{x - 3}$

$$\frac{9}{x + 3} = \frac{5}{x - 3}$$

Perform the cross-product and solve for x.

$$9(x - 3) = 5(x + 3)$$

$$9x - 27 = 5x + 15$$

$$4x - 27 = 15$$

$$4x = 42$$

$$x = 10\tfrac{1}{2} \text{ m.p.h.}$$

Exercise Set 7.6

1.) Mary can paint a bedroom in 6 hours. Joan can paint the
    same bedroom in 4 hours. How long should it take them
    to paint the bedroom if they work together?

2.) Mr. Dunham can unload a freight truck in 5 hours. Mr.
     Smith can unload the same freight truck in 7 hours.
     How long will it take them to unload the freight truck
     if they work together?

3.) What number multiplied by the numerator and added to
     the denominator of the fraction 3/7 makes the resulting
     fraction 12/11?

-194-

4.) What number multiplied by the numerator and added to the denominator of 1/5 makes the resulting fraction ½?

5.) The speed of an airplane in no wind is 250 m.p.h. If the plane travels 150 miles with a tailwind (pushing the plane) in the same amount of time that it travels 130 miles against the headwind, find the speed of the wind.

6.) The speed of a boat in still water is 12 miles per hour. It takes the same amount of time for the boat to travel 6 miles downstream (with the current) as it does to travel 2 miles upstream (against the current). Find the speed of the current.

7.) Two trains leave at the same time and travel along parallel routes. One train travels at 20 m.p.h. faster than the other. If the faster train travels 180 miles in the same time the slower train travels 120 miles, what is the speed of the faster train?

8.) Two runners run along the same course. One runner runs at 5 m.p.h., the other travels at 4 m.p.h. If it takes the slower runner 1/2 longer than the faster runner to complete the course, how long is the course?

Solution to Exercise Set 7.6

1.) 2.4 hours

2.) $2 \frac{11}{12}$ hours or 2 hours and 55 minutes.

3.) 4

4.) 5

5.) $17 \frac{6}{7}$ m.p.h.

6.) 6 m.p.h.

7.) 60 m.p.h.

8.) 10 miles

Section 7.7   Variation

Summary:
_____

Direct Variation

The general form of a direct variation is

$$x = ky$$

where **k** is a constant called the **constant
of proportionality** or the variation constant.
_____

Example 1.   The area of a circle varies directly as the
square of the radius of the circle. Write the
equation of the area of the circle if the constant of proportionality is π.

Solution: $A = kr^2$ (Area varies directly as r^2)
$A = \pi r^2$ (Constant of proportionality is π)

Example 2.   **x** varies directly as **y**. If $x = 20$ when $y = 4$,
find x when $y = 25$.

Solution: Since the constant of proportionality is not
given, we must first find **k**, the constant of
proportionality.

$$x = ky$$

$$20 = k(4)$$

$$20 = 4k$$

$$5 = k$$

Now use $k = 5$ to find x when $y = 25$.

$$x = ky$$

$$x = 5(25)$$

$$x = 125$$

Thus, $x = 125$ when $y = 25$.

Summary:
_____

Inverse Variation

The general form of an inverse variation is

$$x = \frac{k}{y} \quad \text{or} \quad xy = k$$
_____

Example 3. x varies inversely as y. If x = 3 when y = 12, find x when y = 36.

Solution: First write the equation and solve for k.

$$x = \frac{k}{y}$$

$$x = \frac{k}{12}$$

$$36 = k$$

Next, find x when y = 36.

$$x = \frac{k}{y}$$

$$x = \frac{36}{36}$$

$$x = 1$$

Summary:
_____

Joint Variation

The general form of a joint variation where **x** varies jointly as **y** and **z** is

$$\mathbf{x = kyz}$$
_____

Example 4.   The volume, V, of a cylinder varies jointly as
            the square of the radius **r** of the cylinder and
            the height **h** of the cylinder. If the volume of a
            cylinder is 400π/3 cubic inches when the radius
            is 5 inches and the height is 4 inches, find the
            volume of the cylinder with radius 10 inches and
            height 2 inches.

Solution: First write the joint variation, then solve for
            k.

            $V = kr^2h$

            $\dfrac{400\pi}{3} = k(5)^2(4)$

            $\dfrac{400\pi}{3} = k(25)(4)$

            $\dfrac{400\pi}{3} = 100k$

            $\dfrac{4\pi}{3} = k$

            Now solve for the volume of a cylinder with
            radius 10.

            $V = kr^2h$

            $V = \dfrac{4\pi}{3}(10)^2(2)$

            $V = \dfrac{800\pi}{3}$

Example 5.   q varies directly as **r** and inversely as **s**.
             If q = 12 when r = 6 and s = 3, find **q** when
             r = 3 and s = 2.

Solution: First write the combination of variation
             equations, then solve for **k**.

$$q = \frac{kr}{s}$$

$$12 = \frac{k(6)}{3}$$

$$12 = 2k$$

$$6 = k$$

Next, solve for **q** when r = 3 and s = 2.

$$q = \frac{kr}{s}$$

$$q = \frac{6(3)}{2}$$

$$q = 9$$

Exercise Set 7.7

1.) **x** varies directly as **y**.
     If x = 16 when y = 2, find x when y = 5.

2.) **A** varies directly as the cube of **s**.
     If A = 32 when s = 2, find A when s = 4.

3.) **t** varies directly as **p**.
     If t = .24 when p = 4, find t when p = 7.

4.) **x** varies inversely as **y**.
     If x = 12 when y = 8, find x when y = 3.

5.) **L** varies inversely as **r**.
     If L = 16 when r = 3, find L when r = 4.

6.) **t** varies jointly as **n** and **c**.
     If t = 7.35 when n = 14 and c = .5, find t when n = 8
     and c = 1.5.

7.) **r** varies jointly as **s** and **t**.
If r = 12 when s = 2 and t = 3, find r when s = 8 and t = 6.

8.) The wattage rating **w** of an appliance varies jointly as the square of the current I and the resistance, **R**.
If the wattage is 1 watt when the current is .1 ampere and the resistance is 100 ohms, find the wattage when the current is .5 ampere and the resistance is 500 ohms.

9.) **q** varies directly as **r** and inversely as **s**.
If q = 100 when r = 5 and s = 2, find q when r = 8 and s = 3.

10.) **w** varies directly as the square of **x** and inversely as **y**.
If w = 20 when x = 4 and y = 5, find w when x = 3 and y = 6.

Solution to Exercise Set 7.7

1.)	40	2.)	256
3.)	.42	4.)	32
5.)	12	6.)	12.6
7.)	96	8.)	125
9.)	320/3	10.)	75/8

Practice Test

Determine the domain of each of the following.

1.) $\dfrac{5}{x - 7}$

2.) $\dfrac{-3x}{x^2 + 3x - 10}$

Write each expression in reduced form.

3.) $\dfrac{x^2}{4x^2 + 3x}$

4.) $\dfrac{x^2 - 4}{x^2 + 7x + 10}$

Multiply as indicated.

5.) $\dfrac{6x^2y}{7xy^3} \cdot \dfrac{14x^2y^4}{12xy}$

6.) $\dfrac{3}{x-5} \cdot \dfrac{5-x}{6}$

7.) $\dfrac{x^2-y^2}{x+2y} \cdot \dfrac{4x+8y}{x-y}$

8.) $\dfrac{x^3-xy^2}{3x} \cdot \dfrac{6x+6y}{x^2+2xy+y^2}$

Divide as indicated.

9.) $\dfrac{3x^2y}{2xy^2} - \dfrac{4x^3y^2}{2x}$

10.) $\dfrac{3x-3y}{x^2+2xy+y^2} - \dfrac{x^2-y^2}{x+y}$

11.) $\dfrac{x^2+3x-10}{x+5} - \dfrac{x^2-4x+4}{x+2}$

Add or subtract as indicated.

12.) $\dfrac{7}{x+3} + \dfrac{4}{x+3}$

13.) $\dfrac{7}{x+3} - \dfrac{5}{x-3}$

14.) $\dfrac{3x+2}{x^2-7x+10} + \dfrac{4}{x-5}$

Simplify the complex fraction.

15.)
$$\frac{2 + \frac{5}{12}}{1 + \frac{3}{4}}$$

16.)
$$\frac{a + \frac{a}{c}}{a - \frac{a}{c}}$$

Solve the equation.

17.) $\frac{x + 3}{3} = \frac{x}{12}$

18.) $\frac{x}{x - 2} + \frac{4x}{8} = \frac{3x}{6}$

19.) It takes Frank 4 hours to mow Mr. Hunt's lawn. It takes Kurt 2 hours to mow the same lawn. How long will it take them together to mow Mr. Hunt's lawn?

20.) **x** varies directly as **y**.
    If x = 60 when y = 15, find x when y = 8.

Solution to Practice Test

1.) $\{x \mid x \neq 7\}$

2.) $\{x \mid x \neq 5, x \neq -2\}$

3.) $\frac{x}{4x + 3}$

4.) $\frac{x - 2}{x + 5}$

5.) $x^2 y$

6.) $-1/2$

7.) $4(x + y)$

8.) $2(x - y)$

9.) $\dfrac{3}{4xy^3}$

10.) $\dfrac{3}{(x + y)^2}$

11.) $\dfrac{x + 2}{x - 2}$

12.) $\dfrac{11}{x + 3}$

13.) $\dfrac{2(x - 18)}{(x + 3)(x - 3)}$

14.) $\dfrac{7x - 6}{(x + 5)(x - 2)}$

15.) $\dfrac{116}{84}$

16.) $\dfrac{c + 1}{c - 1}$

17.) −4

18.) 0

19.) 4/3 hours

20.) 32

Chapter 8   Roots, Radicals and Complex Numbers

Section 8.1   Radicals and Rational Exponents

Summary:

The **principal** or **positive square root** of a positive real number **x**, written $\sqrt{x}$, is that **positive** number whose square equals **x**.

Example 1.   Find   a.) $\sqrt{81}$ b.) $\sqrt{\dfrac{16}{49}}$

Solution: a.) $\sqrt{81} = 9$ b.) $\sqrt{\dfrac{16}{49}} = \dfrac{4}{7}$

Summary:

Let **a** be a real number and **n** be a positive integer

Table 1

	n IS EVEN	n IS ODD
a is a positive real number	$\sqrt[n]{a}$ is a positive real number	$\sqrt[n]{a}$ is a positive real number
a is a **negative** real number	$\sqrt[n]{a}$ is not a real no. (is imaginary)	$\sqrt[n]{a}$ is a negative real number
a is **0**	$\sqrt[n]{0} = 0$	$\sqrt[n]{0} = 0$

Example 2.   Find   a.) $\sqrt[3]{8}$

b.) $\sqrt[3]{-8}$

c.) $\sqrt[4]{64}$

d.) $\sqrt[4]{-64}$

e.) $-\sqrt[5]{32}$

Solution: a.) $\sqrt[3]{8} = 2$

b.) $\sqrt[3]{-8} = -2$

c.) $\sqrt[4]{64} = 4$

d.) $\sqrt[4]{-64} = $ imaginary number

e.) $-\sqrt[5]{32} = -(2) = -2$

Summary:

$\sqrt{a^2} = |a|$ for any real number a.

Example 3.   Find   a.) $\sqrt{6^2}$

b.) $\sqrt{(-6)^2}$

c.) $\sqrt{(-11)^2}$

d.) $\sqrt{(x + 3)^2}$

e.) $\sqrt{(y - 5)^2}$

-205-

Solution:

a.) $\sqrt{6^2} = |6| = 6$

b.) $\sqrt{(-6)^2} = |-6| = 6$

c.) $\sqrt{(-11)^2} = |-11| = 11$

d.) $\sqrt{(x + 3)^2} = |x + 3|$

e.) $\sqrt{(y - 5)^2} = |y - 5|$

Summary:

1. For nonnegative number **a** and **n** a positive integer

$$\sqrt[n]{a} = a^{1/n}$$

2. For nonnegative number **a** and **m** and **n** integers, **n** $\neq$ **0**,

power

$$\sqrt[n]{a^m} = \left(\sqrt[n]{a}\right)^m = a^{m/n} \quad \text{index}$$

Example 4. Write each of the following in exponential form and then simplify.

a.) $\sqrt{16^4}$

b.) $\left(\sqrt[3]{2}\right)^6$

c.) $\sqrt{x^6}$

d.) $\left(\sqrt[4]{y}\right)^8$

-206-

Solution: a.) $\sqrt{16^4} = 16^{4/2} = 16^2 = 256$

b.) $\left(\sqrt[3]{2}\right)^6 = 2^{6/3} = 2^2 = 4$

c.) $\sqrt{x^6} = x^{6/2} = x^3$

d.) $\left(\sqrt[4]{y}\right)^8 = y^{8/4} = y^2$

Exercise Set 8.1

Evaluate.

1.) $\sqrt{49}$ 2.) $\sqrt[5]{243}$

3.) $\sqrt{(-8)^2}$ 4.) $\sqrt{(21)^2}$

5.) $\sqrt{(x-4)^2}$ 6.) $\sqrt{(y-9)^2}$

Write in exponential form and then simplify.
Assume all variables represent positive real numbers.

7.) $\sqrt[4]{8^{12}}$ 8.) $\sqrt[5]{7^{10}}$

9.) $\sqrt[12]{y^{12}}$ 10.) $\sqrt[5]{x^{75}}$

Solution to Exercise Set 8.1

1.) 7   2.) 3

3.) 8   4.) 21

5.) $|x-4|$ 6.) $|y-9|$

7.) 512   8.) 49

9.) y 10.) x^{15}

Section 8.2 Multiplying and Simplifying Radicals

Summary:

Product Rule for Radicals

For natural number **n**, and real numbers **a** and **b**, not both negative

$$\sqrt[n]{a} \cdot \sqrt[n]{b} = \sqrt[n]{ab}$$

Example 1. Factor a.) $\sqrt{40}$ b.) $\sqrt{y^5}$

Solution: a.) $\sqrt{40} = \sqrt{1} \cdot \sqrt{40}$

$= \sqrt{2} \cdot \sqrt{20}$

$= \sqrt{4} \cdot \sqrt{10}$

$= \sqrt{5} \cdot \sqrt{8}$

b.) $\sqrt{y^5} = \sqrt{y} \sqrt{y^4}$

$= \sqrt{y^2} \sqrt{y^3}$

Summary:

A number is a **perfect square** if it is the square of a natural number.

A number is a **perfect cube** if it is a cube of a natural number.

Summary:

To Simplify Radicals, Without Fractions, Containing Only Numerical Values

1. Write the number as the product of its largest perfect factor and another factor.

2. Use the product rule to write the expression as a product of roots.

3. Find the roots of any perfect factors.

Example 2. Simplify a.) $\sqrt{40}$

                                         b.) $\sqrt{45}$

                                         c.) $\sqrt{162}$

Solution:

                                         a.) $\sqrt{40} = \sqrt{4}\ \sqrt{10}$

$$= 2\sqrt{10}$$

                                         b.) $\sqrt{45} = \sqrt{9}\ \sqrt{5}$

$$= 3\sqrt{5}$$

                                       c.) $\sqrt{162} = \sqrt{81}\ \sqrt{2}$

$$= 9\sqrt{2}$$

Summary:

To Simplify Radicals Containing Variables in the Radicand

1. Write each number and variable in the radicand as a product of its largest perfect factor and another factor.

2. Use the Product Rule to write the expression as a product of roots. All the perfect factors may be placed under the same radical.

3. Simplify the root containing the perfect factors.

Example 3. Simplify

$$\text{a.) } \sqrt{y^5} \qquad \text{b.) } \sqrt[3]{x^7} \qquad \text{c.) } \sqrt{x^3 y^5} \qquad \text{d.) } \sqrt{32 x^5 y^7}$$

Solution: a.) $\sqrt{y^5} = \sqrt{y^4}\,\sqrt{y}$

$$= y^2 \sqrt{y}$$

b.) $\sqrt[3]{x^7} = \sqrt[3]{x^6}\,\sqrt[3]{x}$

$$= x^2 \sqrt[3]{x}$$

c.) $\sqrt{x^3 y^5} = \sqrt{x^2 y^4}\,\sqrt{xy}$

$$= x y^2 \sqrt{xy}$$

d.) $\sqrt{32 x^5 y^7} = \sqrt{16 x^4 y^6}\,\sqrt{2xy}$

$$= 4 x^2 y^3 \sqrt{2xy}$$

Example 4. Multiply and Simplify.

$$\sqrt[3]{9x^4}\ \sqrt[3]{9x^5}$$

Solution: $\sqrt[3]{9x^4}\ \sqrt[3]{9x^5} = \sqrt[3]{81x^9}$

$$= \sqrt[3]{27x^9}\ \sqrt[3]{3}$$

$$= 3x^3\ \sqrt[3]{3}$$

Exercise Set 8.2

Simplify each expression.
Assume that all variables represent positive real numbers.

1.) $\sqrt{18}$

2.) $\sqrt{72}$

3.) $\sqrt[4]{x^5}$

4.) $\sqrt[6]{y^8}$

5.) $\sqrt{20x^4y^7}$

6.) $\sqrt[3]{16x^4y^7}$

7.) $\sqrt[4]{32x^4y^{12}}$

8.) $\sqrt{8}\ \sqrt{7}$

9.) $\sqrt{20x^3y}\ \sqrt{6x^2y^2}$

10.) $\sqrt[3]{8x^2y^3}\ \sqrt[3]{27x^4y}$

Solution to Exercise Set 8.2

1.) $3\sqrt{2}$

2.) $6\sqrt{2}$

3.) $x\sqrt[4]{x}$

4.) $y\sqrt[6]{y^2}$

5.) $2x^2y^3\sqrt{5y}$

6.) $2xy^2\sqrt[3]{2xy}$

7.) $2xy^3\ \sqrt[4]{2x}$

8.) $2\sqrt{14}$

9.) $2x^2y\sqrt{30xy}$

10.) $6x^2y\sqrt[3]{y}$

Section 8.3 Dividing and Simplifying Radicals

Summary:

Quotient Rule for Radicals

For natural number **n**, and real numbers **a** and **b**, not both negative, $b \neq 0$,

$$\frac{\sqrt[n]{a}}{\sqrt[n]{b}} = \sqrt[n]{\frac{a}{b}}$$

Example 1. Simplify a.) $\dfrac{\sqrt{12}}{\sqrt{3}}$

b.) $\dfrac{\sqrt[3]{125}}{\sqrt[3]{5}}$

c.) $\sqrt[3]{\dfrac{64}{27}}$

d.) $\sqrt[3]{\dfrac{200}{25}}$

Solution: a.) $\dfrac{\sqrt{12}}{\sqrt{3}} = \sqrt{\dfrac{12}{3}} = \sqrt{4} = 2$

b.) $\dfrac{\sqrt[3]{125}}{\sqrt[3]{5}} = \sqrt[3]{\dfrac{125}{5}} = \sqrt[3]{25}$

c.) $\sqrt[3]{\dfrac{64}{27}} = \dfrac{\sqrt[3]{64}}{\sqrt[3]{27}} = \dfrac{4}{3}$

d.) $\sqrt[3]{\dfrac{200}{25}} = \sqrt[3]{8} = 2$

Summary:

A Radical is Simplified When the Following Are All True

1. There are no perfect factors in any radicand, and;

2. No radicand contains fractions, and;

3. There are no radicals in any denominator.

    To rationalize a denominator, multiply both the numerator and the denominator of the fraction by the denominator, or by a radical that will result in the radicand in the denominator becoming a perfect factor.

Example 2.   Simplify   a.) $\dfrac{1}{\sqrt{2}}$ b.) $\sqrt{\dfrac{1}{3}}$

   c.) $\sqrt{\dfrac{2}{5}}$ d.) $\sqrt[3]{\dfrac{2}{3}}$

   e.) $\sqrt{\dfrac{1}{x}}$

Solution: a.) $\dfrac{1}{\sqrt{2}} = \dfrac{1}{\sqrt{2}} \cdot \dfrac{\sqrt{2}}{\sqrt{2}} = \dfrac{\sqrt{2}}{2}$

   b.) $\dfrac{1}{\sqrt{3}} = \dfrac{\sqrt{1}}{\sqrt{3}} \cdot \dfrac{\sqrt{3}}{\sqrt{3}} = \dfrac{\sqrt{3}}{3}$

   c.) $\dfrac{2}{\sqrt{5}} = \dfrac{\sqrt{2}}{\sqrt{5}} \cdot \dfrac{\sqrt{5}}{\sqrt{5}} = \dfrac{\sqrt{10}}{5}$

   d.) $\sqrt[3]{\dfrac{2}{3}} = \dfrac{\sqrt[3]{2}}{\sqrt[3]{3}} \cdot \dfrac{\sqrt[3]{3^2}}{\sqrt[3]{3^2}} = \dfrac{\sqrt[3]{2}\,\sqrt[3]{9}}{\sqrt[3]{3^3}} = \dfrac{\sqrt[3]{18}}{3}$

   e.) $\dfrac{1}{\sqrt{x}} = \dfrac{\sqrt{1}}{\sqrt{x}} \cdot \dfrac{\sqrt{x}}{\sqrt{x}} = \dfrac{\sqrt{x}}{x}$

Example 3. Simplify   a.) $\sqrt{\dfrac{4x}{3y}}$ b.) $\sqrt{\dfrac{8x}{5yz}}$

Solution: a.) $\sqrt{\dfrac{4x}{3y}} = \dfrac{\sqrt{4x}}{\sqrt{3y}} = \dfrac{\sqrt{4x}}{\sqrt{3y}} \cdot \dfrac{\sqrt{3y}}{\sqrt{3y}}$

$$= \dfrac{2\sqrt{3xy}}{3y}$$

b.) $\sqrt{\dfrac{8x}{5yz}} = \dfrac{\sqrt{8x}}{\sqrt{5yz}} \cdot \dfrac{\sqrt{5yz}}{\sqrt{5yz}}$

$$= \dfrac{\sqrt{40xyz}}{5yz}$$

$$= \dfrac{2\sqrt{10xyz}}{5yz}$$

Summary:

When the denominator of a rational expression is a binomial which contains a radical, we again rationalize the denominator.

We do this by multiplying both the numerator and the denominator of the fraction by the **conjugate** of the denominator.

The conjugate of a binomial is a binomial having the same two terms with the sign of the second term changed.

Example 4. Simplify $\dfrac{2}{3 + \sqrt{x}}$

Solution: Multiply both numerator and denominator of the fraction by the conjugate of the denominator, $3 - \sqrt{x}$.

$$\dfrac{2}{3 + \sqrt{x}} \cdot \dfrac{3 - \sqrt{x}}{3 - \sqrt{x}} = \dfrac{6 - 2\sqrt{x}}{9 - x}$$

-214-

Exercise Set 8.3

Simplify each expression.
Assume all variables represent positive real numbers.

1.) $\sqrt{\dfrac{125}{5}}$

2.) $\sqrt{\dfrac{9}{16}}$

3.) $\sqrt[3]{\dfrac{27}{125}}$

4.) $\sqrt{\dfrac{x^2}{y^4}}$

5.) $\sqrt[3]{\dfrac{x^9}{y^6}}$

Rationalize the denominator.

6.) $\dfrac{1}{\sqrt{7}}$

7.) $\dfrac{x}{\sqrt{3}}$

8.) $\sqrt{\dfrac{4}{7}}$

9.) $\sqrt{\dfrac{x^3}{y}}$

10.) $\dfrac{8}{3 + \sqrt{y}}$

Solution to Exercise Set 8.3

1.) 5

2.) $\dfrac{3}{4}$

3.) $\dfrac{3}{5}$

4.) $\dfrac{x}{y^2}$

5.) $\dfrac{x^3}{y^2}$

6.) $\dfrac{\sqrt{7}}{7}$

7.) $\dfrac{x\sqrt{3}}{3}$

8.) $\dfrac{x\sqrt{xy}}{y}$

9.) $\dfrac{x\sqrt{xy}}{y}$

10.) $\dfrac{24 - 8y}{9 - y}$

Section 8.4 Addition and Subtraction of Radicals

Summary:

To Add or Subtract Radicals

1. Simplify each radical expression.

2. Combine like radicals (if there are any).

Example 1. Simplify each of the following.

      a.) $2\sqrt{2} - \sqrt{2} + 5\sqrt{2}$

      b.) $4\sqrt[3]{x} + 3\sqrt[3]{x} - 7$

Solution: a.) $2\sqrt{2} - \sqrt{2} + 5\sqrt{2} = 6\sqrt{2}$

          b.) $4\sqrt[3]{x} + 3\sqrt[3]{x} - 7 = 7\sqrt[3]{x} - 7$

-216-

Example 2. Simplify $\sqrt{2} + \sqrt{8} - \sqrt{32}$.

Solution: First simplify $\sqrt{8} = 2\sqrt{2}$ and $\sqrt{32} = 4\sqrt{2}$.

Now $\sqrt{2} + \sqrt{8} - \sqrt{32} = \sqrt{2} + 2\sqrt{2} - 4\sqrt{2}$

$$= -\sqrt{2}$$

Example 3. Simplify $\sqrt{x^2 y} + 2\sqrt{x^2 y} - \sqrt{x^2}$.

Solution: $\sqrt{x^2 y} + 2\sqrt{x^2 y} - \sqrt{x^2} = x\sqrt{y} + 2x\sqrt{y} - x$

$$= 3x\sqrt{y} - x$$

Exercise Set 8.4

Simplify each of the following.

1.) $6\sqrt{2} - 3\sqrt{2} + 2\sqrt{2}$

2.) $7\sqrt[3]{4} - 6\sqrt[3]{4} + 11\sqrt[3]{4}$

3.) $5\sqrt[7]{x} + 11\sqrt[7]{x} - 4\sqrt[7]{x}$

4.) $\sqrt{12} + \sqrt{27}$

5.) $6\sqrt{3} + \sqrt{27} - \sqrt{75}$

6.) $\sqrt{20} - 6\sqrt{5} + \sqrt{125}$

7.) $8\sqrt{x} + \sqrt{4x} - \sqrt{9x}$

8.) $\sqrt{x^3} + x\sqrt{x} + \sqrt{4x^3}$

9.) $\sqrt{25x^2} + \sqrt{9x^2} + \sqrt{7x^2}$

10.) $\sqrt[3]{3x^3} + \sqrt[3]{81x^6} - 4\sqrt{3}$

Solution to Exercise Set 8.4

1.) $5\sqrt{2}$

2.) $12\sqrt[3]{4}$

3.) $12\sqrt[7]{x}$

4.) $5\sqrt{3}$

5.) $4\sqrt{3}$

6.) $3\sqrt{5}$

7.) $7\sqrt{x}$

8.) $4x\sqrt{x}$

9.) $8x + x\sqrt{7}$

10.) $x\sqrt{3} + 3x^2\sqrt{3} - 4\sqrt{3}$

or

$(3x^2 + x - 4)\sqrt{3}$

Section 8.5 Solving Radical Equations

Summary:

To Solve Radical Equations

1. Rewrite the equation so that one radical containing a variable is isolated by itself on one side of the equation.

2. Raise each side of the equation to a power equal to the index of the radical.

3. Collect and combine like terms.

4. If the remaining equation still contains a term with a variable in a radicand, repeat steps 1 through 3.

5. Solve the resulting equation for the unknown variable.

6. Check all solutions in the original equations for extraneous roots.

Example 1. Solve the equation $\sqrt{x} = 8$.

Solution: The square root containing the variable is already by itself on one side of the equation. Square both sides of the equation.

$$\sqrt{x} = 8$$

$$(\sqrt{x})^2 = (8)^2$$

$$x = 64$$

Check:

$$\sqrt{x} = 8$$

$$\sqrt{64} = 8$$

$$8 = 8 \qquad \text{True}$$

Example 2. Solve the equation $\sqrt{x + 3} - 8 = 0$.

Solution: Isolate the radical containing the variable on one side of the equation.

$$\sqrt{x + 3} - 8 = 0$$

$$\sqrt{x + 3} = 8$$

Next, square both sides of the equation and solve for **x**.

$$(\sqrt{x + 3})^2 = (8)^2$$

$$x + 3 = 64$$

$$x = 61$$

Check your solution in the original equation.

Example 3.   Solve the equation $\sqrt{4x + 1} = x - 1$.

Solution: $\sqrt{4x + 1} = x - 1$

Square both sides of the equation and solve for x.

$$(\sqrt{4x + 1})^2 = (x - 1)^2$$

$$4x + 1 = x^2 - 2x + 1$$

$$1 = x^2 - 6x + 1$$

$$0 = x^2 - 6x$$

$$0 = x(x - 6)$$

Either $x = 0$ or $x - 6 = 0$

$x = 6$

Checking: if $x = 0$ if $x = 6$

$\sqrt{4x + 1} = x - 1$ $\sqrt{4x + 1} = x - 1$

$\sqrt{4(0) + 1} = 0 - 1$ $\sqrt{4(6) + 1} = 6 - 1$

$\sqrt{1} = -1$ False $\sqrt{25} = 5$

$5 = 5$ True

The 6 is a solution but the 0 is not a solution to the equation. 0 does not check and is called an extraneous root.

Exercise Set 8.5

Solve each equation and check your solution(s). If the
equation has no real solution, state so.

1.) $\sqrt{x} = 3$

2.) $\sqrt{x} = 11$

3.) $\sqrt{3x + 4} = 4$

4.) $\sqrt{9x + 3} = 5\sqrt{3}$

5.) $\sqrt{6x - 5} + 5 = 10$

6.) $\sqrt{2x + 3} - 5 = 0$

7.) $\sqrt{x + 4} = x - 2$

8.) $\sqrt{2x + 6} = x - 9$

9.) $\sqrt{2x - 3} = x - 9$

10.) $\sqrt{3x + 4} = x - 12$

Solution to Exercise Set 8.5

1.) 9

2.) 121

3.) 4

4.) 8

5.) 5

6.) 11

7.) 5

8.) 15

9.) 14

10.) 20

Section 8.6 Applications of Radicals (optional)

Summary:

Pythagorean Theorem

The square of the hypotenuse of a right triangle is equal to
the sum of the squares of the two legs. If **a** and **b**
represent the legs and **c** represents the hypotenuse, then

$$a^2 + b^2 = c^2$$

Example 1.   Find the hypotenuse of a right triangle whose
             legs are 5 m. and 12 m.

Solution: Draw a picture of the problem before using the
             formula.

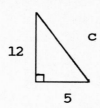

$$a^2 + b^2 = c^2$$

$$5^2 + 12^2 = c^2$$

$$25 + 144 = c^2$$

$$169 = c^2$$

$$\sqrt{169} = \sqrt{c^2}$$

$$13 = c \qquad \text{The hypotenuse is 13 m.}$$

Example 2.   The hypotenuse of a right triangle is 7 feet.
             One leg of the right triangle is 4 feet.

             Find the length of the other leg of the right
             triangle.

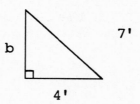

$$a^2 + b^2 = c^2$$

$$4^2 + b^2 = 7^2$$

$$16 + b^2 = 49$$

$$b^2 = 33$$

$$\sqrt{b^2} = \sqrt{33}$$

$$b = \sqrt{33}$$

Summary:

_____

Distance Formula point $A(x_1, y_1)$ and point $B(x_2, y_2)$ then

$$d = \sqrt{x_2 - x_1)^2 + (y_2 - y_1)^2}$$

_____

Example 3. Find the distance between $A(3, 5)$ and $B(6, 8)$.

Solution: $d = \sqrt{(x_2 - x_1)^2 + (y_2 - y_1)^2}$

$d = \sqrt{(6 - 3)^2 + (8 - 5)^2}$

$d = \sqrt{(3)^2 + (3)^2}$

$d = \sqrt{9 + 9}$

$d = \sqrt{18}$

$d = \sqrt{9 \cdot 2}$

$d = 3\sqrt{2}$

Exercise Set 8.6

Find the hypotenuse of a right triangle if the legs are:

1.)   5 and 7

2.)   10 and 24

3.)   8 and 13

Find the leg of a right triangle if the hypotenuse and other leg are respectively:

4.)   20 and 11

5.)   17 and 8

6.)   26 and 10

Find the distance between points A and B if:

7.) A(5, -2) and B(6, -4)

8.) A(3, 11) and B(8, 4)

Solution to Exercise Set 8.6

1.) $\sqrt{74}$ 2.) 26

3.) $\sqrt{233}$ 4.) $\sqrt{279}$

5.) 15   6.) 24

7.) $\sqrt{5}$ 8.) $\sqrt{74}$

Section 8.7 Complex Numbers.

Summary:

Any number of the form **bi**, where **b** is any nonzero real number and $i = \sqrt{-1}$, is an **imaginary number**.

For example, 3i and $i\sqrt{7}$ are imaginary numbers.

Complex Number

Every number of the form   **a + bi**   is a complex number.

Example 1. Write each of the following as complex numbers in the form a + bi.

        a.) $\sqrt{-9}$

        b.) $3 + \sqrt{-8}$

        c.) $2 + \sqrt{-25}$

        d.) $8 - \sqrt{-50}$

Solution: a.) $\sqrt{-9} = \sqrt{9}\,\sqrt{-1}$

$$= 3i$$

        b.) $3 + \sqrt{-8}\ = 3 + \sqrt{8}\,\sqrt{-1}$

$$= 3 + 2\sqrt{2}\,\sqrt{-1}$$

$$= 3 + 2\sqrt{2}\ i$$

        c.) $2 + \sqrt{-25} = 2 + \sqrt{25}\,\sqrt{-1}$

$$= 2 + 5i$$

        d.) $8 - \sqrt{-50} = 8 - \sqrt{50}\,\sqrt{-1}$

$$= 8 - 5\sqrt{2}\ i$$

Note:

    $i^2 = -1$

Summary:

To Add (or Subtract) Complex Numbers

1. Change all imaginary numbers to **bi** form.

2. Add (or subtract) the real parts of the complex numbers.

3. Add (or subtract) the imaginary parts of the complex numbers.

4. Write the answer in the form **a + bi**.

Example 2.   Perform the indicated operation.

$$\text{a.)} \quad (6 + 3i) + (-8 - 14i)$$

$$\text{b.)} \quad (16 + 4i) - (12 + \sqrt{-9})$$

Solution: a.) $(6 + 3i) + (-8 - 14i)$

$$= 6 + 3i - 8 - 14i$$

$$= 6 - 8 + 3i$$

$$= -2 - 11i$$

b.) $(16 + 4i) - (12 + \sqrt{-9})$

$$= (16 + 4i) - (12 + \sqrt{9}\,\sqrt{-1})$$

$$= (16 + 4i) - (12 + 3i)$$

$$= 16 + 4i - 12 - 3i$$

$$= 4 + i$$

Summary:

To Multiply Complex Numbers

1. Change all imaginary numbers to **bi** form.

2. Multiply the complex numbers as you would multiply polynomials.

3. Substitute −1 for each i^2.

4. Combine the real parts and imaginary parts then write the answer in **a + bi** form.

Example 3. Multiply a.) $(2 + 4i)(6 + 3i)$

b.) $(3 - \sqrt{-27})(4 - 3\sqrt{3}i)$

Solution: a.) Multiply by using the FOIL Method.

$$(2 + 4i)(6 + 3i) = 12 + 6i + 24i + 12i^2$$

$$= 12 + 30i + 12(-1)$$

$$= 12 + 30i - 12$$

$$= 30i$$

b.) $(3 - \sqrt{-27})(4 - 3\sqrt{3}i)$

$$= (3 - \sqrt{27}\,\sqrt{-1})(4 - 3\sqrt{3}i)$$

$$= (3 - 3\sqrt{3}i)(4 - 3\sqrt{3}i)$$

$$= 12 - 9\sqrt{3}i - 12\sqrt{3}i + 9\sqrt{9}i^2$$

$$= 12 - 21\sqrt{3}i + 27(-1)$$

$$= 12 - 21\sqrt{3}i - 27$$

$$= -15 - 21\sqrt{3}i$$

Note:

The **conjugate** of a complex number **a** + **bi** is **a** − **bi**.

Summary:

To Divide Complex Numbers

1. Change all imaginary numbers to **bi** form.

2. Write the division problem as a fraction.

3. Rationalize the denominator of the fraction by multiply-
    ing both the numerator and denominator of the fraction
    by the conjugate of the denominator.

4. Write the answer in **a** + **bi** form.

Example 4.   Divide $\dfrac{4 + 3i}{2 - 2i}$

Solution: Multiply both numerator and denominator by
            2 + 2i, which is the conjugate of 2 − 2i.

$$\frac{4 + 3i}{2 - 2i} \cdot \frac{2 + 2i}{2 + 2i} = \frac{8 + 8i + 6i + 6i^2}{4 - 4i^2}$$

$$= \frac{8 + 14i + 6(-1)}{4 - 4(-1)}$$

$$= \frac{2 + 14i}{8}$$

$$= \frac{1 + 7i}{4}$$

-228-

Exercise Set 8.7

Perform the indicated operation.

1.) $(6 + 2i) + (8 - 13i)$

2.) $(3 + \sqrt{-16}) + (4 + \sqrt{-25})$

3.) $(8 + 4i) - (6 + 8i)$

4.) $(8 - \sqrt{-25}) - (4 - \sqrt{-9})$

5.) $(6 + 4i) - (8 + \sqrt{-16})$

6.) $(3 + 2i)(5 - 6i)$

7.) $(3 + \sqrt{-49})(5 + \sqrt{-81})$

8.) $\dfrac{8 + 5i}{6 + 2i}$

9.) $\dfrac{3 + \sqrt{-36}}{2 - \sqrt{-16}}$

10.) $(8 + 4i)(11 - \sqrt{-121})$

Solution to Exercise Set 8.7

1.) $14 - 11i$ 2.) $7 + 9i$

3.) $2 - 4i$ 4.) $4 + 8i$

5.) -2 6.) $27 - 8i$

7.) $-48 + 62i$ 8.) $\dfrac{29 + 7i}{20}$

9.) $\dfrac{-9 + 12i}{10}$ 10.) $132 - 44i$

Section 8.8   The Square Root Function   (optional)

Summary:

_____

 Square Root Function

$$f(x) = \sqrt{x}, \quad x \geq 0$$

for any algebraic expression **x**.

_____

Example 1.   Find the domain of

$$f(x) = \sqrt{x + 2}.$$

Solution: Find the values of **x** that will result in the
radicand being greater than or equal to zero.

Set $x + 2 \geq 0$ and solve for **x**.

$$x \geq -2$$

Domain: $D = \{x \mid x \geq -2\}$.

Example 2.   Graph the function $f(x) = \sqrt{x + 2}$ and state its
range.

Solution: Since the domain of the fraction is the set of
real numbers greater than or equal to -2, use
values of $x \geq -2$ that make $x + 2$ a perfect
square.

x	y
-2	0
-1	1
2	2
7	3

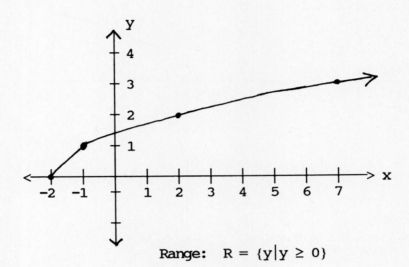

Range: $R = \{y | y \geq 0\}$

Exercise Set 8.8

Find the domain of the following functions.
Graph the function and state its range.

1.) $f(x) = \sqrt{x - 5}$

2.) $f(x) = -\sqrt{x + 2}$

3.) $f(x) = \sqrt{2 - x}$

4.) $f(x) = \sqrt{2x + 4}$

5.) $f(x) = -\sqrt{3x + 6}$

Solution to Exercise Set 8.8

1.) Domain: {x|x ≥ 5}

Range: {y|y ≥ 0}

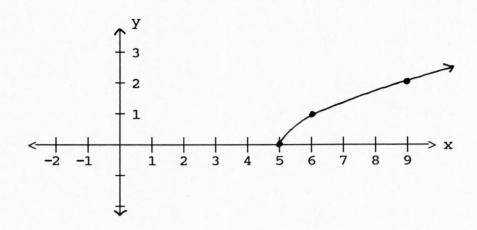

2.) Domain: {x|x ≥ -2}

Range: {y|y ≤ 0}

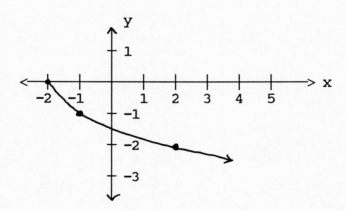

3.) Domain: {x|x ≤ 2}

Range: {y|y ≥ 0}

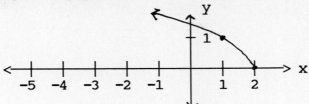

4.) Domain: {x|x ≥ -2}

Range: {y|y ≥ 0}

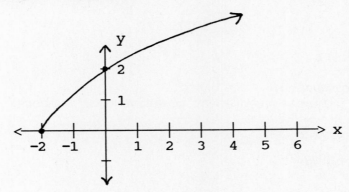

5.) Domain: {x|x ≥ -2}

Range: {y|y ≤ 0}

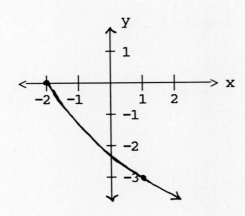

Practice Test

Evaluage each expression.
Assume all variables represent positive real numbers.

1.) $\sqrt{196}$

2.) $\sqrt[4]{625}$

3.) $\sqrt{(-9)^2}$

4.) $\sqrt{(x - 3)^2}$

5.) $\sqrt{60}$

6.) $\sqrt{48}$

7.) $\sqrt{8x^2y^3}$

8.) $\sqrt{\dfrac{64x^2}{16y^4}}$

Rationalize the denominator.
Assume that all variables represent positive real numbers.

9.) $\sqrt{\dfrac{3}{7}}$

10.) $\sqrt{\dfrac{9}{x}}$

Simplify each expression.
Assume that all variables represent positive real numbers.

11.) $\sqrt{8} + 4\sqrt{32} - \sqrt{128}$

12.) $(4 + \sqrt{2})(7 - \sqrt{2})$

13.) $\dfrac{x}{x + \sqrt{2}}$

14.) $\dfrac{x}{2 + \sqrt{x}}$

15.) $\sqrt{x^2y^3} + 2\sqrt{x^2y^5} - 3\sqrt{x^2y^3}$

Solve each equation and check your solution.

16.) $\sqrt{x} = 21$

17.) $\sqrt{x} - 9 = 8$

Perform the indicated operation.

18.) $(7 + \sqrt{-49}) + (8 + 3i)$

19.) $\dfrac{7 + 4i}{3 + 2i}$

State the domain of the function.

20.) $f(x) = \sqrt{2x - 10}$

Solution to Practice Test

1.) 14

2.) 5

3.) 9

4.) $|x - 3|$

5.) $2\sqrt{15}$

6.) $4\sqrt{3}$

7.) $2xy\sqrt{2y}$

8.) $\dfrac{8x}{4y^2}$

9.) $\dfrac{\sqrt{21}}{7}$

10.) $\dfrac{3\sqrt{x}}{x}$

11.) $10\sqrt{2}$

12.) $26 + 3\sqrt{2}$

13.) $\dfrac{x(x - \sqrt{2})}{x^2 - 2}$

14.) $\dfrac{x(2 - x)}{4 - x}$

15.) $(2xy^2 - 2xy)\sqrt{y}$

16.) 441

17.) 73

18.) $15 + 10i$

19.) $\dfrac{29 - 2i}{13}$

20.) $\{x \mid x \geq 5\}$

Chapter 9   Quadratic Equations and Inequalities

Section 9.1   Solving Quadratic Equation by Completing the
              Square

Summary:

Square Root Property

If $x^2 = a$ then $\sqrt{x^2} = \pm \sqrt{a}$ and $x = \pm \sqrt{a}$

Example 1.   Solve the following equations.

a.) $x^2 - 36 = 0$

b.) $x^2 + 5 = 85$

Solution: a.)   Add 36 to both sides of the equation to get
                   the variable on one side of the equation.

$$x^2 - 36 = 0$$

$$x^2 = 36$$

Now take the square root of both sides of
the equation.

$$\sqrt{x^2} = \pm \sqrt{36}$$

$$x = \pm 6$$

b.) $x^2 + 5 = 85$

$$x^2 = 80$$

$$\sqrt{x^2} = \pm \sqrt{80}$$

$$x = \pm \sqrt{16} \sqrt{5}$$

$$x = \pm 4\sqrt{5}$$

Example 2. Solve the equation $(x - 9)^2 = 20$.

Solution: Take the square root of both sides of the equation and solve for x.

$$(x - 9)^2 = 20$$

$$\sqrt{(x - 9)^2} = \pm \sqrt{20}$$

$$x - 9 = \pm \sqrt{4}\,\sqrt{5}$$

$$x - 9 = \pm 2\sqrt{5}$$

$$x = 9 \pm 2\sqrt{5}$$

Summary:

To Solve a Quadratic Equation by Completing the Square

1. Use the multiplication (or division) property if necessary to make the numerical coefficient of the squared term equal to 1.

2. Rewrite the equation with the constant by itself on the right side of the equation.

3. Take one-half the numerical coefficient of the first-degree term, square it, and add this quantity to both sides of the equation.

4. Replace the trinomial with its equivalent squared binomial.

5. Take the square root of both sides of the equation.

6. Solve for the variable.

7. Check your answers in the original equation.

Example 3.   Solve the equation $x^2 + 8x + 1$ by completing the square.

Solution: Since the numerical coefficient of the squared term is 1, add -1 to both sides of the equation to get the constant by itself on the right side of the equation.

$$x^2 + 8x + 1 = 0$$

$$x^2 + 8x = -1$$

The square of one-half the numerical coefficient of the first degree term is $(4)^2 = 16$. Add 16 to both sides of the equation.

$$x^2 + 8x + 16 = -1 + 16$$

$$x^2 + 8x + 16 = 15$$

Factor the left-hand side of the equation.

$$x^2 + 8x + 16 = 15$$

$$(x + 4)^2 = 15$$

Take the square root of both sides of the equation.

$$\sqrt{(x + 4)^2} = \pm \sqrt{15}$$

$$x + 4 = \pm \sqrt{15}$$

$$x = -4 \pm \sqrt{15}$$

Exercise Set 9.1

Solve the equation.

1.) $x^2 - 16 = 0$

2.) $x^2 - 100 = 0$

3.) $x^2 - 4 = 45$

4.) $x^2 - 9 = 25$

5.) $x^2 + 7 = 48$

Solve the following by completing the square.

6.) $x^2 + 6x + 1 = 0$

7.) $x^2 + 8x + 4 = 0$

8.) $x^2 + 10x + 2 = 0$

9.) $x^2 - 4x - 12 = 0$

10.) $x^2 - 2x + 3 = 0$

Solution to Exercise Set 9.1

1.) ± 4 2.) ± 10

3.) ± 7 4.) $\pm \sqrt{34}$

5.) $\pm \sqrt{41}$ 6.) $-3 \pm 2\sqrt{2}$

7.) $-4 \pm 2\sqrt{3}$ 8.) $-5 \pm \sqrt{23}$

9.) 0 and -8 10.) $1 \pm 2i$

Section 9.2 Solving Quadratic Equations by the Quadratic Formula.

Summary:

To Solve a Quadratic Equation by the Quadratic Formula

1. Write the quadratic equation in standard form,

$$ax^2 + bx + c = 0,$$

and determine the numerical values for **a**, **b**, and **c**.

2. Substitute the values for **a**, **b**, and **c** in the quadratic formula then evaluate the formula to obtain the solution.

The quadratic formula

$$x = \frac{-b \pm \sqrt{b^2 - 4ac}}{2a}$$

Example 1. Solve the equation $x^2 - 3x - 18 = 0$ by the quadratic formula when $a = 1$, $b = -3$, and $c = -18$.

Solution:

$$x = \frac{-b \pm \sqrt{b^2 - 4ac}}{2a}$$

$$x = \frac{-(-3) \pm \sqrt{(-3)^2 - 4(1)(-18)}}{2(1)}$$

$$x = \frac{3 \pm \sqrt{9 + 72}}{2}$$

$$x = \frac{3 \pm \sqrt{81}}{2}$$

$$x = \frac{3 \pm 9}{2}$$

$$x = \frac{3 + 9}{2} \quad\quad \text{or} \quad\quad x = \frac{3 - 9}{2}$$

$$x = \frac{12}{2} \quad\quad \text{or} \quad\quad x = \frac{-6}{2}$$

$$x = 6 \quad\quad \text{or} \quad\quad x = -3$$

The solutions are $x = 6$ and $x = -3$.

Example 2. Solve the equation $2x^2 - 3x + 9 = 0$ using the quadratic formula when $a = 2$, $b = -3$, and $c = 9$.

Solution:

$$x = \frac{-b \pm \sqrt{b^2 - 4ac}}{2a}$$

$$x = \frac{-(-3) \pm \sqrt{(-3)^2 - 4(2)(9)}}{2(2)}$$

$$x = \frac{3 \pm \sqrt{9 - 72}}{4}$$

$$x = \frac{3 \pm \sqrt{-63}}{4}$$

$$x = \frac{3 \pm \sqrt{9}\sqrt{7}\sqrt{-1}}{4}$$

$$x = \frac{3 \pm 3\sqrt{7}\,i}{4}$$

Summary:

Discriminant

For a quadratic equation of the form $ax^2 + bx + c = 0$, $a \neq 0$ the discriminant is $b^2 - 4ac$.

If $b^2 - 4ac > 0$, then the quadratic equation has two distinct real solutions.

If $b^2 - 4ac = 0$, then the quadratic equation has a single real solution (also called a double root.)

If $b^2 - 4ac < 0$, then the quadratic equation has no real solution.

Example 3. Determine whether each equation has two distinct real solutions, a single real solution or no real solution.

   a.) $x^2 - 3x - 18 = 0$

   b.) $2x^2 - 3x + 9 = 0$

Solution: a.) $a = 1$, $b = -3$, and $c = -18$

$$b^2 - 4ac = (-3)^2 - 4(1)(-18)$$

$$= 9 + 72$$

$$= 81$$

Since the discriminant is positive, there are two real solutions.

   b.) $a = 2$, $b = -3$, and $c = 9$

$$b^2 - 4ac = (-3)^2 - 4(2)(9)$$

$$= 9 - 72$$

$$= -63$$

Since the discriminant is negative, there are no real solutions.

-241-

Exercise Set 9.2

Determine whether each equation has two distinct real solutions, a single real solution, or no real solution.

1.) $x^2 + 3x + 2 = 0$

2.) $x^2 + 3x - 8 = 0$

3.) $2x^2 + 4x + 3 = 0$

4.) $3x^2 + 2x + 1 = 0$

5.) $x^2 + 6x + 9 = 0$

Use the quadratic formula to solve the equation.

6.) $x^2 + 3x + 2 = 0$

7.) $x^2 + 3x - 8 = 0$

8.) $2x^2 + 4x + 3 = 0$

9.) $3x^2 + 2x + 1 = 0$

10.) $x^2 + 6x + 9 = 0$

Solution to Exercise Set 9.2

1.) Two real solutions.

2.) Two real solutions.

3.) No real solution.

4.) No real solution.

5.) One real solution.

6.) -1 and -2

7.) $\dfrac{-3 + \sqrt{43}}{2}$ and $\dfrac{-3 - \sqrt{43}}{2}$

8.) $-2 + \sqrt{2}\,i$ and $-2 - \sqrt{2}\,i$

9.) $-1 + \sqrt{2}\,i$ and $-1 - \sqrt{2}\,i$

10.) -3

Section 9.3 Quadratic Inequalities in One Variable

Example 1. Graph the solution set to the inequality
$x^2 + x \leq 0$.

Solution: $x^2 + x - 6 \leq 0$

$(x + 3)(x - 2) \leq 0$

To find out where each factor equals 0, we can
set each factor to 0 and solve.

$x + 3 = 0$ $\qquad\qquad$ $x - 2 = 0$

$\quad x = -3$ $\qquad\qquad\quad$ $x = 2$

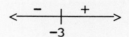 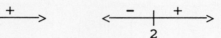

Determining the sign of the product of the
numbers in each region.

When $x < -3$, both factors are negative making the
product of the factors greater than 0.

When $-3 < x < 2$, $x + 3$ is positive and $x - 2$ is
negative making the product of the factors negative.

When $x > 2$, both factors are positive and their
product is positive.

Thus our solution is $-3 \leq x \leq 2$ as graphed below.

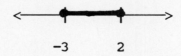

Example 2. Solve the inequality $(x + 1)(x - 2)(x - 4) > 0$
and graph the solution on the number line.

Solution: We will need 3 number lines since we have three
factors.

$$x + 1 = 0 \qquad\qquad x - 2 = 0 \qquad\qquad x - 4 = 0$$

$$x = -1 \qquad\qquad x = 2 \qquad\qquad x = 4$$

If all three factor as positive, then their
product is positive.

If two of the factors are negative and the
third factor is positive then their product
is positive.

Example 3. Solve the inequality $\dfrac{x - 2}{x + 3} \le 0$ and

graph the solution on the number line.

Solution: $x - 2 = 0 \qquad\qquad x + 3 = 0$

$$x = 2 \qquad\qquad\qquad x = -3$$

Since $\dfrac{x - 2}{x + 3} \le 0$ then $-3 \le x \le 2$.

-244-

Exercise Set 9.3

Solve each inequality and graph the solution on a number line.

1.) $x^2 - 9 > 0$

2.) $x^2 - 5x + 6 \leq 0$

3.) $x^2 - 6x + 8 \geq 0$

4.) $2x^2 + 6x + 4 \leq 0$

5.) $(x + 3)(x + 1)(x + 2) \geq 0$

6.) $(x + 4)(x + 2)(x - 3) \geq 0$

7.) $\dfrac{x - 2}{x + 3} < 0$

8.) $\dfrac{x + 4}{x - 3} > 0$

Solution to Exercise Set 9.3

1.) $x < -3$ or $x > 3$

2.) $2 \leq x \leq 3$

3.) $x \leq 2$ or $x \geq 4$

4.) $-2 \leq x \leq -1$

5.) $-3 \leq x \leq -2$ or $x \geq -1$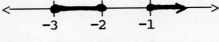

6.) $-4 \leq x \leq -2$ or $x \geq 3$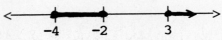

7.) $-3 < x < 2$

8.) $x < -4$ or $x > 3$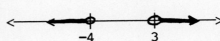

-245-

Section 9.4 Quadratic Functions

Summary:

Quadratic Function

$$f(x) = ax^2 + bx + c, \ a \neq 0$$

Axis of Symmetry of Parabola

For an equation of the form $y = ax^2 + bx + c, \ a \neq 0$, axis of symmetry of the parabola is

$$x = \frac{-b}{2a}$$

Coordinates of Vertex of a Parabola

For an equation of the form $y = ax^2 + bx + c, \ a \neq 0$, the coordinates of the vertex of the parabola are

$$\frac{-b}{2a} \ , \ \frac{4ac - b^2}{4a}$$

Roots of a Quadratic Equation

To find the roots of an equation of the form

$$y = ax^2 + bx + c, \ a \neq 0$$

Set $y = 0$ and solve for x.

Example 1. Consider the equation $2x^2 - 5x - 8 = 0$.

        a.) Determine whether the parabola opens upward or downward;

        b.) find the y intercept;

        c.) find the vertex;

        d.) find the roots if they exist;

        e.) sketch the graph.

Solution: a.) Since a = 2, which is greater than 0, the parabola opens upward.

b.) $y = 2(0)^2 - 5(0) - 8 = -8$, therefore the y intercept is -8.

c.)
$$x = -\frac{b}{2a} \qquad\qquad y = \frac{4ac - b^2}{4a}$$

$$= \frac{-(-5)}{2(2)} \qquad\qquad = \frac{4(2)(-8) - (-5)^2}{4(2)}$$

$$= \frac{5}{4} \qquad\qquad = \frac{-64 - 25}{8}$$

$$\qquad\qquad\qquad\qquad = \frac{-69}{8}$$

The vertex is $\frac{5}{4}, \frac{-69}{8}$.

d.) The trinomial cannot be factored. Use the determinant to determine if there are any real roots.

$$b^2 - 4ac = (-5)^2 - 4(2)(-8)$$

$$= 25 + 64$$

$$= 39$$

Since the discriminant is greater than 0, the equation has two real roots.

$$x = \frac{-b \pm \sqrt{b^2 - 4ac}}{2a}$$

$$x = \frac{-(-5) \pm \sqrt{(-5)^2 - 4(2)(-8)}}{2(2)}$$

$$x = \frac{5 \pm \sqrt{25 + 64}}{4}$$

$$x = \frac{5 \pm \sqrt{89}}{4}$$

$$x = \frac{5 + \sqrt{89}}{4} \approx 14.4$$

$$x = \frac{5 - \sqrt{89}}{4} \approx -4.4$$

e.)

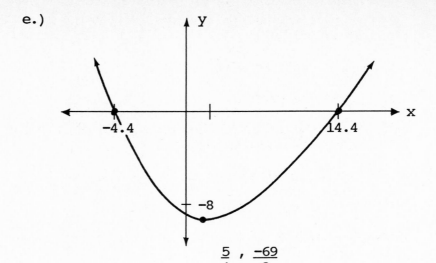

$$\frac{5}{4} , \frac{-69}{8}$$

Example 2. Write an equation in two variables that have roots of 4 and -2.

Solution: If the roots are 4 and -2, the factors must be (x - 4) and (x + 2). Therefore, the equation is:

$$y = (x - 4)(x + 2)$$

$$y = x^2 - 2x - 8$$

Note: There are other forms of the equation

$$y = x^2 - 2x - 8$$

which has the same roots such as

$$y = 2x^2 - 4x - 16$$

$$y = 5x^2 - 10x - 40$$

$$y = ax^2 - ax - 8a$$

where $a \neq 0$.

Exercise Set 9.4

    a.) Determine whether the parabola opens upward or downward;

    b.) find the y intercept;

    c.) find the vertex;

    d.) find the roots if they exist (use a calculator to help make approximations);

    e.) sketch the graph.

1.) $y = x^2 - 6x + 8$

2.) $y = x^2 + 4x - 21$

3.) $y = 4x^2 - 8x + 3$

4.) $y = x^2 - 2x - 24$

Write an equation in two variables that has the roots given.

5.) -3, 5

6.) -1, -7

7.) ½, ½

8.) 2, -4

Solution to Exercise Set 9.4

1.) a.) upward
      b.) + 8
      c.) (3, -17)
      d.) 2, 4

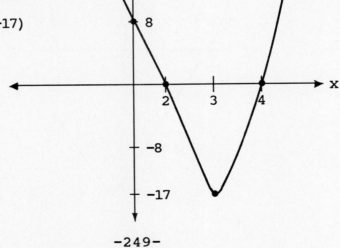

2.) a.) upward
    b.) -21
    c.) (-2, -25)
    d.) -7, 3

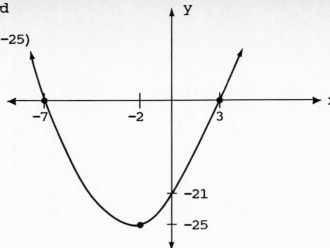

3.) a.) upward
    b.) 3
    c.) (1, -1)
    d.) $\frac{1}{2}$, $\frac{3}{2}$

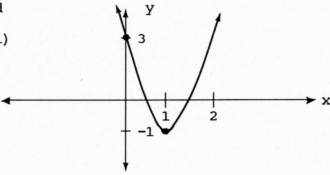

4.) a.) upward
    b.) -24
    c.) (1, -25)
    d.) -4, 6

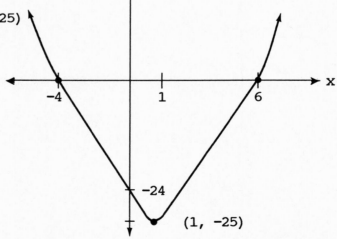

(1, -25)

5.) $y = x^2 - 2x - 15$

6.) $y = x^2 + 8x + 7$

7.) $y = x^2 + x + \frac{1}{4}$

8.) $y = x^2 + 2x - 8$

Practice Test

Solve each equation by completing the square.

1.) $x^2 + 8x - 1 = 0$

2.) $x^2 - 4x + 2 = 0$

3.) $x^2 - 3x - 8 = 0$

Determine whether the equation has two distinct real solutions, a single real solution or no real solution.

4.) $x^2 + 3x - 9 = 0$

5.) $2x^2 - 5x + 7 = 0$

6.) $-4x^2 + 3x + 8 = 0$

Solve by the quadratic formula.

7.) $x^2 + 3x - 9 = 0$

8.) $x^2 - 4x + 2 = 0$

9.) $-4x^2 + 3x + 8 = 0$

Solve each inequality and graph the solution on the number line.

10.) $x^2 - 6x + 5 < 0$

11.) $3x^2 - 5x + 2 > 0$

12.) $\dfrac{x - 2}{x + 7} < 0$

13.) $(x + 3)(x - 4)(x + 4) > 0$

14.) $\dfrac{x - 6}{x + 3} \geq 0$

15.) $(x + 3)(x + 3)(x - 3) \leq 0$

      a.)   Determine whether the parabola opens upward or downward;

      b.)   find the y intercept;

      c.)   find the vertex;

      d.)   find the roots of the equation if they exist and;

      e.)   sketch the graph.

16.) $y = -x^2 + 3x - 3$

17.) $y = 2x^2 + 4x + 2$

18.) $y = x^2 - 6x + 5$

Write an equation in two variables that have the following roots.

19.) $-3, -6$

20.) $8, -4$

Solution to Practice Test

1.) $-4 \pm \sqrt{17}$

2.) $2 \pm \sqrt{2}$

3.) $\dfrac{3}{2} \pm \dfrac{\sqrt{34}}{2}$

4.) Two real solutions.

5.) No real solution.

6.) No real solution.

7.) $\dfrac{-3 \pm 3\sqrt{5}}{2}$

8.) $2 \pm \sqrt{2}$

9.) $\dfrac{-3 \pm \sqrt{137}}{8}$

10.)

    ←———|——————|——————→
         1   5

11.)

    ←——⟨——|——————|——⟩——→
         $-\frac{1}{3}$ 2

12.)

    ←——●━━━━━━●——→
       −7   2

13.)

    ←——●━━●━━●━━→→
      −4 −3

14.)

    ←——|———●━━━→
      −3   6

15.)

    ←——◀━━━━━●——→
      −3   3

16.)   a.) downward
        b.) −3
        c.) (3/2, −3/4)
        d.) No real roots

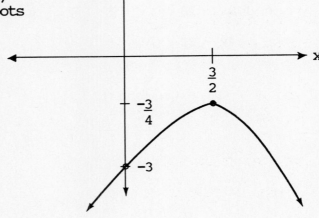

17.) a.) upward
      b.) +2
      c.) (-1, 0)
      d.) One real solution -1.

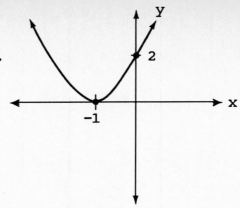

18.) a.) upward
      b.) +5
      c.) (3, -4)
      d.) 1, 5

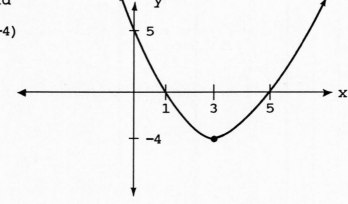

19.) $y = x^2 + 9x + 18$

20.) $y = x^2 - 4x - 32$

Chapter 10   Conic Sections

Section 10.1   The Circle

Summary:
_____

Circle with Center at the Origin and Radius r

$$x^2 + y^2 = r^2$$
_____

Example 1.   Write the equation of a circle with center at
             (0, 0) and radius 5.

Solution: The radius 5 should be substituted into the
             equation for r.

$$x^2 + y^2 = r^2$$

$$x^2 + y^2 = 5^2$$

$$x^2 + y^2 = 25$$

Summary:
_____

Circle with Center at (h, k) and Radius r

$$(x - h)^2 + (y - k)^2 = r^2$$
_____

Example 2.   a.)   Determine the equation of the circle with
                   center at (3, 4) and radius 2.

             b.)   Sketch the circle.

Solution: a.)   The center is (3, 4). Thus h = 3 and k = 4.
                  The radius, r, is 2.

$$(x - h)^2 + (y - k)^2 = r^2$$

$$(x - 3)^2 + (y - 4)^2 = 2^2$$

$$(x - 3)^2 + (y - 4)^2 = 4$$

           b.)

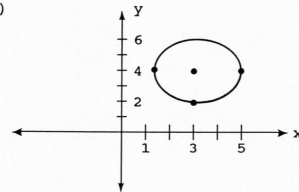

Example 3. a.)   Show that the equation
                   $x^2 + 4x + y^2 - 6y - 12 = 0$
                   is the equation of a circle.

           b.)   Determine the center and radius of the
                   circle.

Solution: a.)   Rewrite the equation placing all terms with
                   variables on one side of the equation and
                   the constant on the other side of the
                   equation.

$$x^2 + 4x + y^2 - 6y - 12 = 0$$

$$x^2 + 4x + y^2 - 6y = 12$$

Complete the square for each variable.

$$x^2 + 4x + 4 + y^2 - 6y = 12 + 4$$

$$x^2 + 4x + 4 + y^2 - 6y + 9 = 12 + 4 + 9$$

$$x^2 + 4x + 4 + y^2 - 6y + 9 = 25$$

-256-

Factor the trinomial in each variable.

$$(x + 2)^2 + (y - 3)^2 = 5^2$$

b.) The center of the circle is (-2, 3) and the radius of the circle is 5.

Exercise Set 10.1

Write the equation of the circle with given center and radius. Then sketch the graph.

1.) Center (0, 0)   radius 2.

2.) Center (-2, -3) radius 2.

3.) Center (-5, 5) radius 3.

4.) Center at the origin with radius 4.

Write the equation of the circle in standard form. State what is the center and radius of the circle.

5.) $x^2 + 2x + y^2 - 2y - 2 = 0$

6.) $x^2 - 6x + y^2 - 4y - 12 = 0$

7.) $x^2 - 2x + y^2 + 8y + 1 = 0$

8.) $x^2 - 10x + y^2 + 6y - 15 = 0$

Solution to Exercise Set 10.1

1.) $x^2 + y^2 = 4$

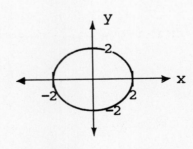

2.) $(x + 2)^2 + (y + 3)^2 = 9$

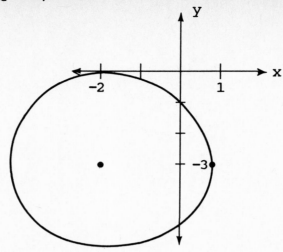

3.) $(x + 5)^2 + (y - 5)^2 = 9$

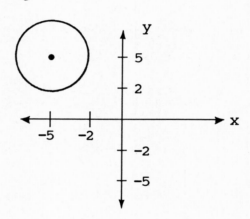

4.) $x^2 + y^2 = 16$

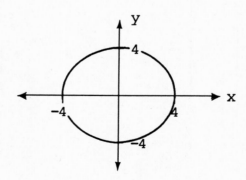

5.) $(x + 1)^2 + (y - 1)^2 = 2^2$
     Center $(-1, 1)$, radius 2.

6.) $(x - 3)^2 + (y - 2)^2 = 5^2$
     Center $(3, 2)$, radius 5.

7.) $(x - 1)^2 + (y + 4)^2 = 4^2$
     Center $(1, -4)$, radius 4.

8.) $(x - 5)^2 + (y + 3)^2 = 7^2$
     Center $(5, -3)$, radius 7.

Section 10.2 The Ellipse

Summary:

Ellipse with Center at the Origin

$$\frac{x^2}{a^2} + \frac{y^2}{b^2} = 1$$

The standard form of an ellipse with its center at origin is

$$\frac{x^2}{a^2} + \frac{y^2}{b^2} = 1$$

where a and $-a$ are the x intercepts and b and $-b$ are the y intercepts.

Example 1. Sketch the graph of $\frac{x^2}{4} + \frac{y^2}{25} = 1$

Solution: Rewrite $\frac{x^2}{4} + \frac{y^2}{25} = 1$

                as $\frac{x^2}{2^2} + \frac{y^2}{5^2} = 1$

The x intercepts are -2 and 2.
The y intercepts are -5 and 5.

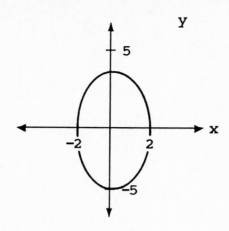

Example 2.   Sketch the graph $4x^2 + 25y^2 = 100$.

Solution: Divide both sides of the equation by 100.

$$\frac{4x^2}{100} + \frac{25y^2}{100} = \frac{100}{100}$$

$$\frac{x^2}{25} + \frac{y^2}{4} = 1$$

The x intercepts are -5 and 5.
The y intercepts are -2 and 2.

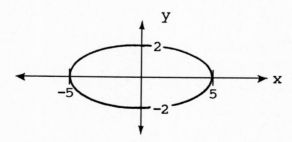

Exercise Set 10.2

Sketch the graph of each equation.

1.) $\dfrac{x^2}{1} + \dfrac{y^2}{9} = 1$

2.) $\dfrac{x^2}{25} + \dfrac{y^2}{36} = 1$

3.) $\dfrac{x^2}{36} + \dfrac{y^2}{16} = 1$

4.) $4x^2 + 9y^2 = 36$

5.) $x^2 + 121y^2 = 121$

Solution to Exercise Set 10.2

1.)

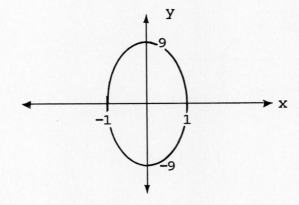

2.)

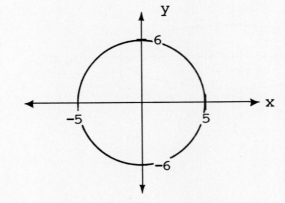

3.)

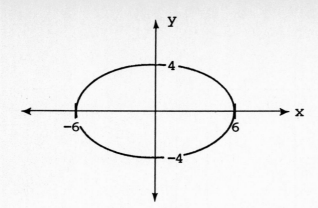

4.)

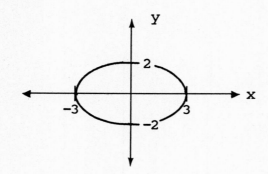

5.)

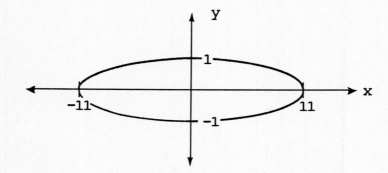

Section 10.3 The Parabola

Summary:

Parabola with Vertex at (h, k)

a.) $y = a(x - h)^2 + k$, $a > 0$ (opens upward)

b.) $y = a(x - h)^2 + k$, $a < 0$ (opens downward)

c.) $x = a(y - k)^2 + h$, $a > 0$ (opens to the right)

d.) $x = a(y - k)^2 + h$, $a < 0$ (opens to the left)

Example 1. Sketch the graph $y = -2(x - 2)^2 + 1$.

Solution: The graph opens downward since $a = -2$, which is
            less than 0.

            The vertex is at $(2, 1)$.
            The y intercept is $-2(0 - 2)^2 + 1 = -7$.

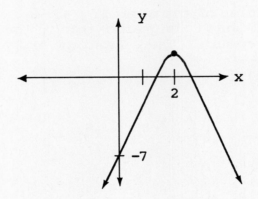

Example 2. a.) Write the equation $y = x^2 + 8x + 8$
                 in $y = a(x - h)^2 + k$ form.

            b.) Sketch the graph of $y = x^2 + 8x + 8$.

Solution: a.) Convert $y = x^2 + 8x + 8$ to $y = a(x - h) + k$ form by completing the square.

$$y = x^2 + 8x + 8$$

Find one-half the coefficient of the x term and square it.

$$\tfrac{1}{2}(8) = 4. \qquad 4^2 = 16.$$

Add + 16 and −16 to the equation to obtain

$$y = x^2 + 8x + 16 - 16 + 8$$

We have created a perfect square plus a constant.

$$y = x^2 + 8x + 16 - 16 + 8$$

$$y = (x + 4)^2 - 8$$

b.) The vertex of the parabola (−4, −8). Since a = 1, which is greater than 0, the graph opens upward. The y intercept is 8.

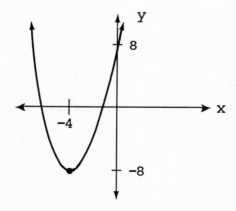

Exercise Set 10.3

Sketch the graph of each equation.

1.) $y = (x - 3)^2 + 1$

2.) $y = (x + 2)^2 - 1$

3.) $x = (y - 2)^2 + 1$

4.) $x = (y + 3)^2 + 2$

Write each in the form $y = a(x - h)^2 + k$ or $x = a(y - k)^2 + h$
State the vertex, whether the graph opens upward, downward,
right or left, and the y or x intercept.

5.) $y = x^2 + 6x + 4$

6.) $y = x^2 - 10x + 8$

7.) $x = y^2 - 2y + 4$

8.) $x = y^2 - 12y + 8$

Solution to Exercise Set 10.3

1.)

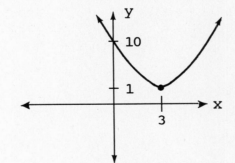

2.)

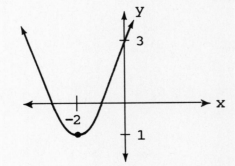

3.)

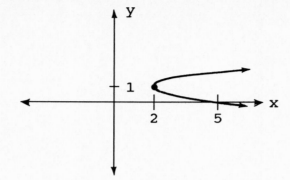

4.)

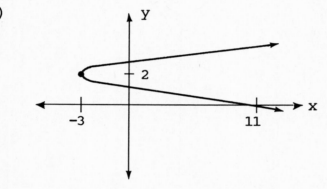

5.) Vertex (-3, 5); opens upward; (0, 4)

6.) Vertex (5, 17); opens upward; (0, 8)

7.) Vertex (1, 3);   opens right; (4, 0)

8.) Vertex (6, -28); opens right; (8, 0)

Section 10.4 The Hyperbola

Summary:

Hyperbola with Center at the Origin

x axis transverse axis   y axis transverse axis

$$\frac{x^2}{a^2} - \frac{y^2}{b^2} = 1$$ $$\frac{y^2}{b^2} - \frac{x^2}{a^2} = 1$$

Asymptotes

$$y = \frac{b}{a}x \qquad \text{and} \qquad y = \frac{b}{a}x$$

Example 1. a.) Determine the equations of the asymptotes of the hyperbola with equation.

$$\frac{x^2}{16} - \frac{y^2}{9} = 1$$

b.) Sketch the hyperbola using asymptotes as aids.

Solution: a.) The value of a^2 is 16; the positive root of 16 is 4. The value of b^2 is 9; the positive root of 9 is 3. The asymptotes are:

$$y = \frac{bx}{a} \quad \text{and} \quad y = \frac{-bx}{a}$$

$$y = \frac{3x}{4} \quad \text{and} \quad y = \frac{-3x}{4}$$

b.) First, graph the asymptotes. Since the x term is positive, the graph intersects the x axis.

Since the denominator of the positive term is 16, the vertices will be at 4 and -4. Draw the hyperbola by letting the hyperbola approach its asymptotes.

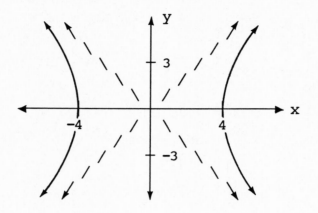

Example 2. a.) Show that the equation $16x^2 - 4y^2 = 64$ is a hyperbola by expressing the equation in standard form.

b.) Determine the asymptotes of the graph.

c.) Sketch the graph.

Solution: a.) Divide both sides of the equation by 64 to get 1 on the right side of the equation.

$$\frac{16x^2 - 4y^2}{64} = \frac{64}{64}$$

$$\frac{x^2}{4} - \frac{y^2}{16} = 1$$

b.) The equation of the asymptotes are
$$y = \frac{4}{2}x \quad \text{and} \quad y = -\frac{4}{2}x$$

or $y = 2x$ and $y = -2x$.

c.) The graph intersects the x axis at -2 and 2.

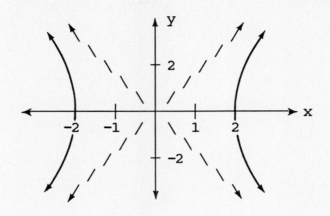

Exercise Set 10.4

Determine the equations of the asymptotes, and sketch the graph of the equation.

1.) $\dfrac{x^2}{4} - \dfrac{y^2}{25} = 1$

2.) $\dfrac{y^2}{16} - \dfrac{x^2}{9} = 1$

3.) $\dfrac{x^2}{49} - \dfrac{y^2}{64} = 1$

4.) $\dfrac{x^2}{16} - \dfrac{y^2}{4} = 1$

Write each equation in standard form and determine the equations of the asymptotes.

5.) $25^2 - y^2 = 100$

6.) $25x^2 - 4y^2 = 100$

7.) $16y^2 - 25x^2 = 400$

8.) $36y^2 - 4x^2 = 144$

Solution to Exercise Set 10.4

1.) $y = \pm \frac{5}{2}x$

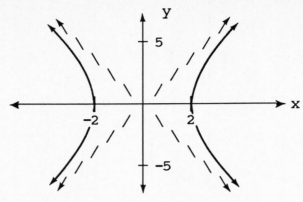

2.) $y = \pm \frac{4}{3}x$

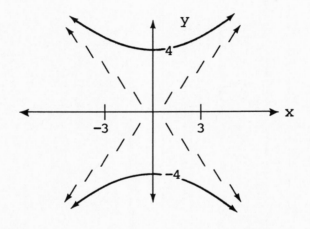

3.) $y = \pm \frac{8}{7}x$

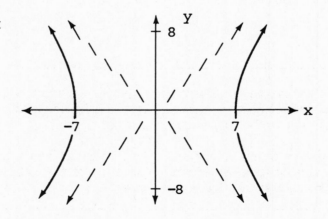

4.) $y = \pm\, 2x$

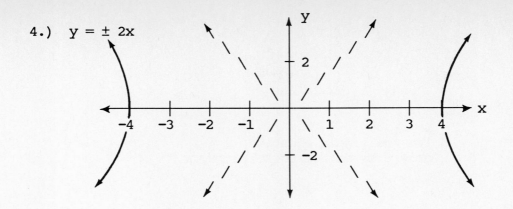

5.) $\dfrac{x^4}{4} - \dfrac{y^2}{100} = 1;\quad y = \pm\, 5x$

6.) $\dfrac{x^2}{4} - \dfrac{y^2}{25} = 1;\quad y = \pm\, \dfrac{5}{2}x$

7.) $\dfrac{y^2}{25} - \dfrac{x^2}{16} = 1;\quad y = \pm\, \dfrac{5}{4}x$

8.) $\dfrac{y^2}{25} - \dfrac{x^2}{36} = 1;\quad y = \pm\, \dfrac{1}{9}x$

Section 10.5   System of Nonlinear Equations

Summary:

A **system of nonlinear equations** is a system of equations containing at least one that is not a linear equation (that is, one whose graph is not a straight line).

To solve a system of equations algebraically, we often solve one or more of the equations for one of the variables, and then use the substitution principle.

Example 1. Solve the system of equations algebraically using substitution.

$$x^2 + y^2 = 4$$

$$x - y = 2$$

Solution: Solve the linear equation, $x - y = 4$, for either x or y. We select to solve for x.

$$x - y = 2$$

$$x = y + 2$$

Substitute $x = y + 4$ for x in the equation $x^2 + y^2 = 4$ and solve for the remaining variable y.

$$x^2 + y^2 = 4$$

$$(y + 2)^2 + y^2 = 4$$

$$y^2 + 4y + 4 + y^2 = 4$$

$$2y^2 + 4y + 4 = 4$$

$$2y^2 + 4y = 0$$

$$2y(y + 2) = 0$$

Either $2y = 0$ or $y + 2 = 0$

$\qquad y = 0 \qquad\qquad\qquad y = -2$

Next, find the corresponding value of x by substituting each value of y in the equation solved for x.

If: $y = 0$ If: $y = -2$

$\qquad x = y + 2 \qquad\qquad\qquad x = y + 2$

$\qquad x = 0 + 2 \qquad\qquad\qquad x = -2 + 2$

$\qquad x = 2 \qquad\qquad\qquad\qquad x = 0$

The solutions are (2, 0) and (0, -2).

Example 2. Solve the following system of equations by the addition method.

$$x^2 - y = 3$$

$$x^2 + y^2 = 9$$

Since both equations contain an x^2 term, we can eliminate the variable x by the addition method.

$$(-1)[x^2 - y] = (3)(-1) \quad \text{gives} \quad -x^2 + y = -3$$
$$x^2 + y^2 = 9 \qquad\qquad\qquad \underline{x^2 + y^2 = 9}$$
$$y^2 + y = 6$$
$$y^2 + y - 6 = 0$$
$$(y + 3)(y - 2) = 0$$

Either $y + 3 = 0$ or $y - 2 = 0$

$$y = -3 \qquad\qquad y = 2$$

Find the corresponding values of x by using the equation $x^2 - y = 3$.

If: $\quad\quad y = -3$ If: $\quad\quad\quad y = 2$

$$x^2 - y = 3 \qquad\qquad x^2 - y = 3$$
$$x^2 - (-3) = 3 \qquad\qquad x^2 - (-2) = 3$$
$$x^2 + 3 = 3 \qquad\qquad\qquad x^2 = 5$$
$$x^2 = 0 \qquad\qquad\qquad x = \pm\sqrt{5}$$
$$x = 0$$

There are three solutions $(0, 3)$, $(\sqrt{5}, 2)$ and $(-\sqrt{5}, 2)$.

Exercise Set 10.5

Solve the system of equations by the substitution method.

1.) $y = x^2 - 6x + 8$

　　$y = x - 2$

2.) $x^2 + y^2 = 25$

　　$3x + 4y = 25$

3.) $x^2 + y^2 = 5$

　　$x^2 = 3y$

4.) $x^2 + y = 2$

　　$x + y = 0$

Solve the system of equations using the addition method.

5.) $x^2 + y^2 = 16$

　　$3x^2 - 2y^2 = 28$

6.) $x^2 + y^2 = 25$

　　$3x + 4y = 25$

7.) $4x^2 - 5y^2 = 16$

　　$3x^2 + 2y^2 = 35$

8.) $x^2 + y = 2$

　　$x + y = 0$

Solution to Exercise Set 10.5

1.) $(1, 3)$, $(6, 8)$

2.) $(3, 4)$

3.) $(\sqrt{3}, 1)$

4.) $(-1, 1)$, $(2, -2)$

5.) $(2\sqrt{3}, 2)$, $(2\sqrt{3}, -2)$, $(-2\sqrt{3}, 2)$, $(-2\sqrt{3}, -2)$

6.) $(3, 4)$

7.) $(2, 3)$, $(2, -3)$, $(-2, 3)$, $(-2, -3)$

8.) $(-1, 1)$, $(2, -2)$

Section 10.6   Systems of Nonlinear Inequalities

Example 1.   Graph the inequality.

$$\frac{x^2}{4} + \frac{y^2}{25} \leq 1$$

Solution: Graph the equation $\frac{x^2}{4} + \frac{y^2}{25} = 1$.

Use a solid line when drawing the ellipse since
the inequality contains $\leq$.

Select a test point not on the graph, such as
(0, 0), and test it in the original inequality.

$$\frac{0^2}{4} + \frac{0^2}{25} \leq 1$$

$$0 + 0 \leq 1$$

$$0 \leq \quad 1 \qquad \text{True}$$

Therefore, the solution set is the ellipse and all points
in the inside of ellipse.

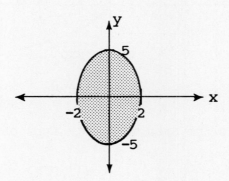

Summary:

To Solve a Nonlinear System of Two Inequalities

1. Graph one inequality.

2. On the same set of axes, draw the second inequality. Use a different type of shading than was used in the first inequality.

3. The solution is the area containing the shaded area from both inequalities.

Example 2.   Solve the system of inequalities graphically.

$$x^2 + y^2 \leq 25$$

$$x \leq y^2$$

Solution: Graph each inequality on the same set of axes.

$x^2 + y^2 \leq 25$ 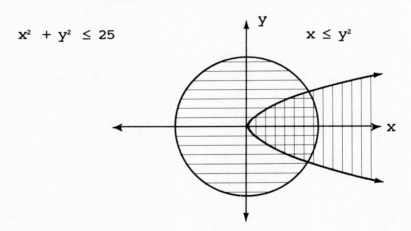 $x \leq y^2$

The solution is the area with both type of shading.

Exercise Set 10.6

Graph each inequality.

1.) $\dfrac{x^2}{25} + \dfrac{y^2}{4} \geq 1$

2.) $\dfrac{x^2}{36} + \dfrac{y^2}{25} \leq 1$

3.) $x^2 + y^2 \geq 4$

Graph each system of nonlinear inequalities.

4.) $x^2 + y^2 \leq 4$

$\qquad\quad y \leq x^2$

5.) $x^2 + y^2 \geq 25$

$\qquad x - y \leq -1$

Solution to Exercise Set 10.6

1.)

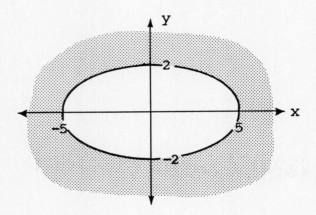

2.)

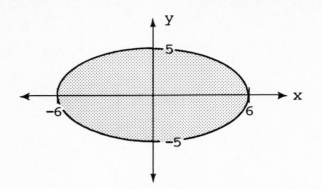

3.)

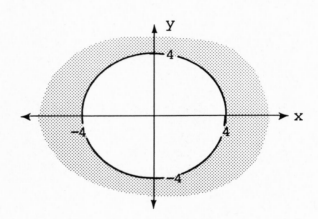

4.)

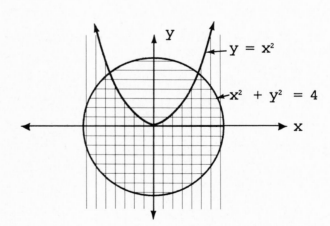

5.)

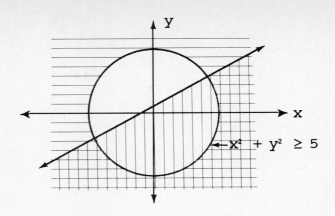

$x^2 + y^2 \geq 5$

Practice Test

Write the equation of the circle in standard form.

1.) Center (0, 0), radius 8.

2.) Center (-1, 3), radius 4.

Sketch the graph of each equation.

3.) $x^2 + y^2 = 49$

4.) $(x - 3)^2 + (y - 2)^2 = 4$

Write the equation of the circle in standard form.

5.) $x^2 - 2x + y^2 - 6y - 26 = 0$

6.) $x^2 + y^2 + 8y = 0$

Sketch the graph of each equation.

7.) $\dfrac{x^2}{81} + \dfrac{y^2}{16} = 1$

8.) $\dfrac{x^2}{1} + \dfrac{y^2}{4} = 1$

Graph each equation.

9.) $y = (x - 3)^2 + 8$

10.) $y = (x + 2)^2 - 4$

Write each equation in the form $y = a(x - h) + k$.

11.) $y = x^2 - 12x$

12.) $y = x^2 + 4x + 9$

Determine the equations of the asymptotes.

13.) $\dfrac{x^2}{36} - \dfrac{y^2}{16} = 1$

14.) $\dfrac{y^2}{81} - \dfrac{x^2}{144} = 1$

Sketch the graph.

15.) $\dfrac{x^2}{36} - \dfrac{y^2}{81} = 1$

16.) $\dfrac{y^2}{49} - \dfrac{x^2}{16} = 1$

Write each equation in standard form and determine the equations of the asymptotes.

17.) $49x^2 - 4y^2 = 196$

18.) $9y^2 - 49x^2 = 441$

Solve the system of equations.

19.) $x^2 + y^2 = 16$

$x + y = -4$

Graph each system of nonlinear inequalities.

20.) $x^2 + y^2 \leq 36$

   $x + y \geq 5$

Solution to Practice Test

1.) $x^2 + y^2 = 64$

2.) $(x + 1)^2 + (y - 3)^2 = 16$

3.)

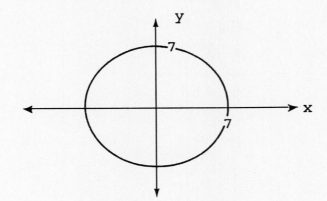

4.)

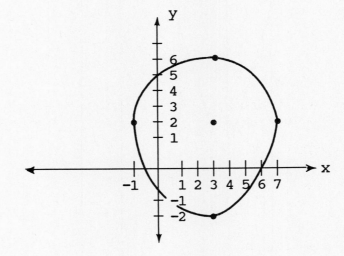

5.) $(x - 1)^2 + (y - 3)^2 = 6^2$

6.) $(x - 0)^2 + (y + 4)^2 = 4^2$

7.)

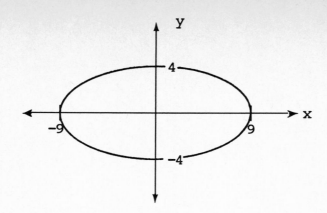

8.)

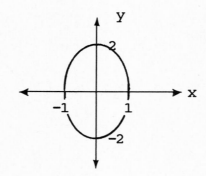

9.)

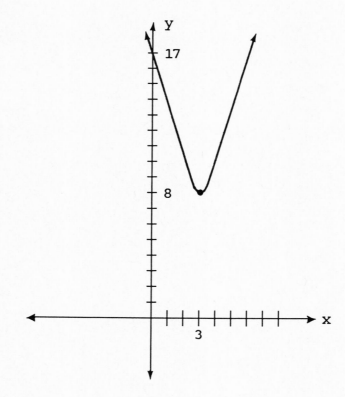

10.)

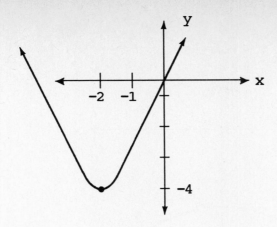

11.) $y = (x - 6)^2 - 36$

12.) $y = (x + 2)^2 + 5$

13.) $y = \pm \frac{2}{3}x$

14.) $y = \pm \frac{3}{4}x$

15.)

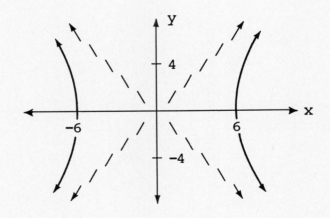

16.)

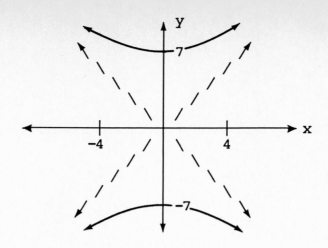

17.) $\frac{x^2}{4} - \frac{y^2}{49} = 1; \quad y = \pm \frac{7}{4}x$

18.) $\frac{y^2}{49} - \frac{x^2}{9} = 1; \quad y = \pm \frac{7}{3}x$

19.) (0, -4), (-4, 0)

20.)

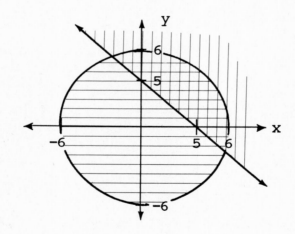

Chapter 11 Exponential and Logarithmic Functions

Section 11.1 Inverse Functions

Summary:

A **one-to-one function** is a function where each **y** value has a
unique **x** value. For a function to be a one-to-one function,
it must pass not only a **vertical line test** (the test to
ensure that it is a function) but also a **horizontal line
test** (to test the one-to-one criterion).

Example 1. Determine which functions are one-to-one
            functions.

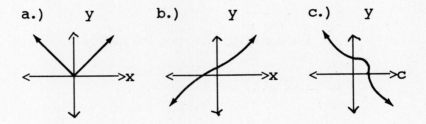

a.)   y   b.)   y   c.)   y

Solution: **b** and **c** are one-to-one functions since they pass
            the vertical line test.   Note that **a, b,** and **c**
            are functions since they pass the horizontal line
            test but only **b** and **c** are one-to-one functions.

Summary:

Inverse Function

If $f(x)$ is a one-to-one function with ordered pairs of the form (x, y), then its inverse function, $f^{-1}(x)$, will be one-to-one function with ordered pairs of the form (y, x).

To Find the Inverse Function
          of One-to-One Functions
                    of the Form $y = f(x)$

1. Interchange the two variables x and y.

2. Solve the equation for y. The resulting equation
    will be the inverse function.

Example 2. Find the inverse function.

a.) $y = 5x - 3$

b.) $y = \dfrac{x - 2}{5}$

Solution: a.) Interchange the two variables x and y, and
                solve for y.

$$f(x) = y = 5x - 3$$

$$x = 5y - 3$$

$$x + 3 = 5y$$

$$\frac{x + 3}{5} = y$$

$$f^{-1}(x) = y = \frac{x + 3}{5}$$

b.) $y = \dfrac{x - 2}{5}$

Interchange the two variables x and y, and solve for y.

$$x = \dfrac{y - 2}{5}$$

$$5x = y - 2$$

$$5x + 2 = y$$

$$f^{-1}(x) = y = 5x + 2$$

Exercise Set 11.1

Determine whether each function is a one-to-one function.

1.)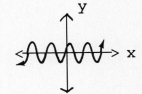

2.)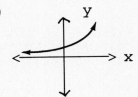

3.)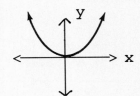

4.)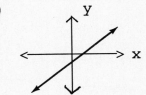

5.)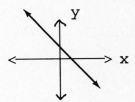

Find the inverse function.

6.) $y = 3x - 9$

7.) $y = 8x + 7$

8.) $y = 5x - 4$

9.) $y = \dfrac{x - 2}{5}$

10.) $y = \dfrac{3x + 4}{5}$

Section 11.2 Exponential and Logarithmic Functions

Summary:

Exponential Function

$$f(x) = a^2$$

for any real number $a > 0$ and $a \neq 1$ is an exponential function.

Example 1. Graph the exponential function $y = 3^x$. State the domain and range of the function.

Solution: Construct a table of values before plotting the points.

x	-3	-2	-1	0	1	2	3
y	$\dfrac{1}{27}$	$\dfrac{1}{9}$	$\dfrac{1}{3}$	1	3	9	27

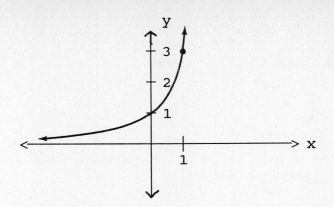

D: {x $\in$ reals}

R: {y|y > 0}

Summary:

Definition of Logarithm

For all positive numbers **a**, where **a** $\neq$ **1**,

$$y = \log_a x \quad \text{means} \quad x = a^y$$

Example 2. Write each of the following in logarithmic form.

     a.) $5^3 = 125$

     b.) $\left(\dfrac{1}{3}\right)^3 = \dfrac{1}{27}$

     c.) $3^{-4} = \dfrac{1}{81}$

Solution: a.) $\log_5 125 = 3$

b.) $\log_{1/3} 1/27 = 3$

c.) $\log_3 1/81 = -4$

Example 3. Write each of the following logarithms in exponential form.

a.) $\log_7 49 = 2$

b.) $\log_4 64 = 3$

c.) $\log_{\frac{1}{2}} 1/16 = 4$

Solution: a.) $7^2 = 49$

b.) $4^3 = 64$

c.) $(\frac{1}{2})^4 = 1\backslash 16$

Example 4. Write each logarithm in exponential form, then find the missing value.

a.) $y = \log_2 32$

b.) $y = \log_3 81$

Solution: a.) $y = \log_2 32$

$2^y = 32$

Since $2^5 = 32$, $y = 5$.

b.) $y = \log_3 81$

$$3^y = 81$$

Since $3^4 = 81$, $y = 4$.

Exercise Set 11.2

1.) Graph the exponential function $y = (\frac{1}{4})^x$.

Write each expression in logarithmic form.

2.) $5^3 = 125$

3.) $6^2 = 36$

4.) $4^{-3} = 1/64$

Write each expression in exponential form.

5.) $\log_5 625 = 4$

6.) $\log_8 64 = 2$

7.) $\log_{\frac{1}{4}} 64 = -3$

Write each logarithm in exponential form then find the missing value.

8.) $\log_7 343 = y$

9.) $\log_{1/3} 9 = y$

10.) $\log_3 x = 4$

Solution to Exercise Set 11.2

1.)

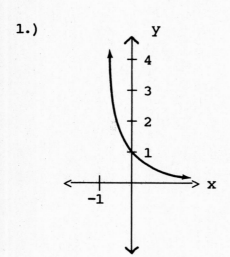

2.) $\log_5 125 = -3$

3.) $\log_6 36 = 2$

4.) $\log_4 1/64 = -3$

5.) $625 = 5^4$

6.) $64 = 8^2$

7.) $64 = (\frac{1}{4})^{-3}$

8.) 3

9.) −2

10.) 81

Section 11.3 Properties of Logarithms

Summary:

Product Rule For Logarithms

For positive real numbers x, y and a, $a \neq 1$,

$$\log_a xy = \log_a x + \log_a y$$ Property 1

Quotient Rule For Logarithms

For positive real numbers x, y and a, $a \neq 1$,

$$\log_a x/y = \log_a y$$ Property 2

Power Rule for Logarithms

If x and a are positive real numbers, $a \neq 1$,
and n is any real number, then

$$\log_a x^n = n \log_a x$$ Property 3

Example 1. Expand each of the following using the properties
of logarithms.

a.) $\log_4 (3 \cdot 7)$

b.) $\log_3 (7 \cdot 6)$

c.) $\log_4 (7/5)$

d.) $\log_7 (4)^3$

Solution: Use the product rule with a = 4, x = 3 and y = 7.

a.) $\log_a xy = \log_a x + \log_a y$

$\log_4 (3 \cdot 7) = \log_4 3 + \log_4 7$

b.) $\log_3 (7 \cdot 6) = \log_3 7 + \log_3 6$

$= \log_3 7 + \log_3 (2 \cdot 3)$

$= \log_3 7 + \log_3 2 + \log_3 3$

$= \log_3 7 + \log_3 2 + 1$

c.)   Use the quotient rule of logarithms with
a = 4, x = 7 and y = 5.

$\log_a x/y = \log_a x - \log_a y$

$\log_4 (7/5) = \log_4 7 - \log_4 5$

d.)   Use the power rule of logarithms with
a = 7, x = 4 and n = 3.

$\log_a x^m = n \log_a x$

$\log_7 (4)^3 = 3 \log_7 4$

Example 2. Write each of the following as a logarithm of a single expression.

     a.) $\log_3 7 + \log_3 8$

     b.) $\log_3 11 - \log_3 10$

     c.) $4 \log_3 2$

Solution: a.) Use the product rule:

$$\log_3 7 + \log_3 8 = \log_3 (7 \cdot 8).$$

           b.) Use the quotient rule:

$$\log_3 11 - \log_3 10 = \log_3 (11/10).$$

           c.) Use the power rule:

$$4 \log_3 2 = \log_3 (2)^4.$$

Exercise Set 11.3

Expand each of the following using the properties of logarithms.

1.) $\log_7 (3 \cdot 9)$

2.) $\log_{11} (10 \cdot 9)$

3.) $\log_{10} (12/7)$

4.) $\log_8 (12)^{11}$

5.) $\log_6 4 \cdot (8)^3$

Write each expression as the logarithm of a single expression.

6.) $\log_3 20 + \log_3 5$

7.) $\log_5 12 - \log_5 8$

8.) $4 \log_5 9$

9.) $3 \log_5 7 + 2 \log_5 3$

10.) $4 \log_3 7 - 21 \log_3 4$

Solution to Exercise Set 11.3

1.) $\log_7 3 + \log_7 9$

2.) $\log_{11} 10 + \log_{11} 9$

3.) $\log_{10} 12 - \log_{10} 7$

4.) $11 \log_8 12$

5.) $\log_6 4 + 3 \log_6 8$

6.) $\log_3 (20 \cdot 5) = \log_3 100$

7.) $\log_5 (12/8) = \log_5 (3/2)$

8.) $\log_5 9^4$

9.) $\log_5 [(7)^4 \cdot (3)^2]$

10.) $\log_3 \left(\dfrac{7^4}{4^{21}}\right)$

Section 11.4 Common Logarithms

Summary:

The common logarithm of a number is the exponent to which
the base 10 is raised to obtain the number.

For any real number **n**

$$\log 10^n = n \qquad \qquad \text{Property 4}$$

Example 1. Find the following logarithms using Appendix D of
the textbook.

    a.) $\log 6.30$

    b.) $\log 6.07$

    c.) $\log 6.49$

Solution: a.) $\log 6.30 = .7782$

          b.) $\log 6.07 = .7832$

          c.) $\log 6.49 = .8122$

Example 2. a.) Find $\log 3,100$.

          b.) Find $\log .000109$.

Solution: To find logarithm of numbers not between 1.00 and
9.99 first write the number in scientific
notation.

Next use the product of property of logarithms to
eventually obtain a numerical answer.

a.) $\log 3,100 = \log (3.1 \cdot 10^3)$

$$= \log 3.1 + \log 10^3$$

$$= \log 3.1 + 3 \log 10$$

$$= .4914 + 3(1)$$

$$= .4914 + 3$$

$$= 3.4914$$

b.) $\log .000109 = \log (1.09 \cdot 10^{-4})$

$$= \log 1.09 + \log 10^{-4}$$

$$= \log 1.09 + (-4) \log 10$$

$$= .0374 + (-4)(1)$$

$$= .0374 + (-4)$$

$$= 6.0374 - 10$$

Summary:

If $\log N = L$ then $N = $ antilog L

Example 3. a.) Find the antilog 4.3032.

b.) If $\log N = 6.4669 - 10$, find N.

Solution: a.) Look up the mantissa .3032 in Appendix D of your textbook. The value from the borders of the table is 2.01. Since the characteristic is 4, move the decimal four places to the right to obtain the answer 20,100.

b.) Since log N = 6.4669 - 10

$$N = antilog\ (6.4669 - 10)$$

$$N = .4669 - 4$$

$$N = 2.93 \cdot 10^{-4}$$

$$N = .000293$$

Exercise Set 11.4

Find the following logarithms.

1.) log 7.04

2.) log 8.91

3.) log 89,100

4.) log .00704

5.) log 8,110,000

Find the antilog of the logarithm.

6.) .4014

7.) 2.5065

8.) 7.9727 - 10

9.) 3,9814

10.) 5.8482 - 10

Solution to Exercise Set 11.4

1.) .8476

2.) .9499

3.) 4.9499

4.) 7.8476 - 10

5.) 6.9090

6.) 2.52

7.) 3.21

8.) .00939

9.) 9580

10.) .0000705

Section 11.5   Exponential and Logarithmic Equations

Summary:

_____

To Solve Exponential and Logarithmic Equations

We may use the properties:

a.)   If $x = y$, then $a^x = a^y$

b.)   If $a^x = a^y$, then $x = y$

c.)   If $x = y$, then $\log x = \log y$ $(x > 0,\ y > 0)$. Property 5

d.)   If $\log x = \log y$, then $x = y$ $(x > 0,\ y > 0)$.

_____

Example 1.   Solve the following equations.

$$\text{a.)}\quad 9^x = 1/3$$

$$\text{b.)}\quad 4^x = 12$$

$$\text{c.)}\quad \log_3 (x + 1)^3 = 5$$

Solution: a.)   Rewrite the equation using exponents and the base 3.

$$9^x = 1/3$$
$$(3^2)^x = 3^{-1}$$
$$3^{2x} = 3^{-1}$$
$$2x = -1$$
$$x = -\tfrac{1}{2}$$

b.) $4^x = 12$

Take the log of each side of the equation.

$$\log 4^x = \log 12$$

$$x \log 4 = \log 12$$

$$x \cdot (.6021) = 1.0792$$

$$x = 1.7924$$

c.) $\log_3 (x + 1)^3 = 5$

Write the equation in exponential form.

$$(x + 1)^3 = 3^5$$

$$(x + 1)^3 = 243$$

$$x + 1 = \sqrt[3]{243}$$

$$x = -1 + \sqrt[3]{243}$$

Example 4. Solve the equation $\log x + \log (x + 2) = \log 15$.

Solution: $\log x + \log (x + 2) = \log 15$.

Write the left side of the equation as the
logarithm of a single expression.

$$\log [x(x + 2)] = \log 15$$

$$x(x + 2) = 15$$

$$x^2 + 2x = 15$$

$$x^2 + 2x - 15 = 0$$

$$(x + 5)(x - 3) = 0$$

$x + 5 = 0$ 　　　　 or 　　　　 $x - 3 = 0$

$x = -5$ 　　　　　　　　　　　 $x = 3$

Check: if x = -5

then x + 2 = -3

log (-5) + log (-3) = log 15

Logarithms of negative numbers are not real numbers. Therefore, x = -5 is an extraneous root.

if x = 3

then x + 2 = 5

log x + log (x + 2) = log 15

log 3 + log 5 = log 15

log (3)(5) = log 15

log 15 = log 15   True

Exercise Set 11.5

Solve the following equations.

1.) $5^X = \dfrac{1}{25}$

2.) $3^X = \dfrac{1}{81}$

3.) $5^X = 100$

4.) $6^X = 18$

5.) $12^X = 6$

6.) $\log x + \log (x + 3) = \log 18$

7.) $\log (15 + x) - \log x = \log 4$

8.) log (3x + 1) = 2

9.) log x + log (x + 4) = 32

10.) 2 log x - log 2 = log 8

Solution to Exercise Set 11.5

1.) -2   2.) -4

3.) 2.8613   4.) 1.6131

5.) .7211   6.) 6

7.) 5   8.) 33

9.) 4   10.) 4

Practice Test

Determine which functions are one-to-one functions.

1.)   y   2.)   y

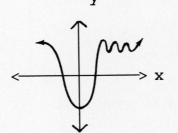   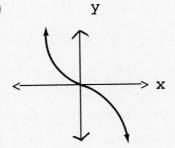

Find $f^{-1}(x)$ given $f(x)$.

3.) $f(x) = 4x - 7$ 4.) $f(x) = \dfrac{x + 2}{3}$

Graph the following functions.

5.) $y = 4^x$ 6.) $y = (1/5)^x$

Write in logarithmic form.

7.) $6^3 = 216$ 8.) $16^{1/4} = 2$

Write in exponential form.

9.) $\log_2 32 = 5$ 10.) $\log_7 2401 = 4$

11.) $\log_8 2 = 1/3$ 12.) $\log_6 1/36 = -2$

Write in exponential form and find the missing value.

13.) $\log_3 2187 = y$ 14.) $\log_4 x = 5$

Use the properties of logarithms to expand each expression.

15.) $\log_4 (5 \cdot 6)$ 16.) $\log_3 (5/8)$

17.) $\log_7 (5)^4$ 18.) $\log_6 x/xy$

19.) Write as the logarithm of a single

$$\log_3 (x - 2) + 4 \log_3 (8 + x).$$

20.) Solve the exponential equation $4.9^x = 38.6768$.

Solution to Practice Test

1.) One-to-one

2.) Not one-to-one

3.) $y = \dfrac{x - 7}{4}$

4.) $y = 3x - 2$

5.)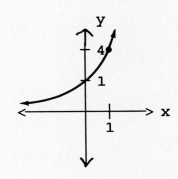

6.)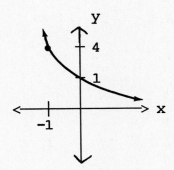

7.) $\log_6 216 = 3$

8.) $\log_{16} 2 = 1/4$

9.) $32 = 2^5$

10.) $2401 = 7^4$

11.) $2 = 8^{1/3}$

12.) $1/36 = 6^{-2}$

13.) 7

14.) 1024

15.) $\log_4 5 + \log_4 6$

16.) $\log_3 5 - \log_3 8$

17.) $4 \log_7 5$

18.) $\log_6 x - [\log_6 x + \log_6 y]$

19.) $\log_3 [(x - 2)(8 + x)^4]$

20.) 2.3

Chapter 12   Sequence, Series and Binomial Theorem

Section 12.1   Sequences and Series

Example 1.   Given the sequence 4, 9, 16, 25, 36,..., find

        a.)   The second term in the sequence.
        b.)   The fourth term in the sequence.
        c.)   The sixth term in the sequence.

Solution: a.)   The second term of the sequence is 9.
        b.)   The fourth term of the sequence is 25.
        c.)   The sixth term of the sequence

$$a_n = (n + 1)^2 \text{ is } 49.$$

Example 2.   Given the sequence $a_n = 4n + 1$, find:

        a.)   The first term in the sequence.
        b.)   The third term in the sequence.
        c.)   The fifth term in the sequence.
        d.)   The twentieth term in the sequence.

Solution: a.)   When $n = 1$, $a_1 = 4(1) + 1 = 5.$

        b.)   When $n = 3$, $a_3 = 4(3) + 1 = 13.$

        c.)   When $n = 5$, $a_5 = 4(5) + 1 = 21.$

        d.)   When $n = 20$, $a_{20} = 4(20) + 1 = 81.$

Example 3. Write the next three terms and the general term for each sequence.

    a.) 50, 45, 40,...

    b.) 160, 80, 40,...

    c.) $\frac{1}{2}$, $\frac{2}{3}$, $\frac{3}{4}$,...

Solution: a.) Each term differs from the previous term by −5. The next three terms are 35, 30, and 25. Since the first term is 50 and each term varies from the previous term by −5, one way of writing the general term is $a_n = -5n + 55$.

    b.) Each term is exactly half of the previous term. The next three terms are 20, 10, and 5. Since the first term was 160 and each term varies from the previous term by one-half, one way of writing $a_n = \dfrac{160}{2^{n-1}}$.

    c.) Form the next term by adding 1 to the numerator and adding one to the denominator of the previous term in the sequence.

$$\frac{1+1}{2+1} = \frac{2}{3} \; ; \; \frac{2+1}{3+1} = \frac{3}{4} \; ; \; \frac{3+1}{4+1} = \frac{4}{5} \; ; \; \frac{4+1}{5+1} =$$

$$\frac{5}{6} \; ; \text{ and } \frac{5+1}{6+1} = \frac{6}{7}.$$

The next three terms in the sequence are

$$\frac{4}{5} \; ; \; \frac{5}{6} \text{ and } \frac{6}{7}.$$

The general term can be expressed as

$$a_n = \frac{n}{n+1}.$$

Example 4. Find the first, third and seventh partial sums
            for the sequence given in Example 1.

Solution: Since the sequence 4, 9, 16, 25, 36, ... has the

            general term $a_n = (n + 1)^2$, the sixth and seventh

            terms in the sequence should be 49 and 64

            respectively.

            $s_1 = 4$

            $s_3 = 4 + 9 + 16 = 29$

            $s_7 = 4 + 9 + 16 + 25 + 36 + 49 + 64 = 203$

Exercise 12.1

Write the first five terms of the sequence whose nth term is
shown.

  1.) $a_n = 3n$

  2.) $a_n = n^3$

  3.) $a_n = \dfrac{n + 1}{2n}$

Find the indicated term of the sequence whose nth term is
shown.

  4.) $a_n = 3n + 2$,   third term

  5.) $a_n = (-3)^n$,   fifth term

  6.) $a_n = n(n + 3)$, seventh term

Find the first, second and third partial sums for the given sequence.

7.) $a_n = 5n + 3$ 8.) $a_n = n(n + 7)$

Write the next three terms of each sequence, then write an expression for the general term of the sequence.

9.) 4, 8, 12, 16, 20,...   10.) 5, 8, 11, 14, 17,...

Solutions to Exercise Set 12.1

1.) 3, 6, 9, 12, 15

2.) 1, 8, 27, 64, 125

3.) 1, $\frac{3}{4}$, $\frac{4}{6}$, $\frac{5}{8}$, $\frac{6}{10}$

4.) $a_3 = 11$

5.) $a_5 = -243$

6.) $a_7 = 70$

7.) $s_1 = 8$

     $s_3 = 39$

8.) $s_1 = 8$

     $s_3 = 56$

9.) 24, 28, 32; $a_n = 4n$

10.) 20, 23, 26; $a_n = 3n + 2$

Section 12.2 Arithmetic Sequences and Series

Example 1. a) Write an expression for the nth term of the arithmetic sequence with first term 23 and a common difference of 8.

b) Find the seventh term of the arithmetic sequence.

Solution: a.) $a_n = a_1 + (n - 1)d$ Substitute $a_1 = 23$
                                         and $d = 8$.

$a_n = 23 + (n - 1)8$

b.) $a_7 = 23 + (7 - 1)8$ Substitute $n = 7$.

$a_7 = 23 + (6)8$

$a_7 = 23 + 48$

$a_7 = 71$

Example 2. Find the number of terms in the arithmetic sequence 103, 101, 99, ..., 51.

Solution: Substitute $a_1 = 51$, $a_n = 51$ and $d = -2$ into

$a_n = a_1 + (n - 1)d$

$51 = 103 + (n - 1)(-2)$	Substitution
$51 = 103 + (-2n + 2)$	Distribute (-2)
$51 = 103 - 2n + 2$	Simplify
$51 = 105 - 2n$	Combine like terms
$-54 = -2n$	Subtraction property
$27 = n$	Division property

-311-

Example 3. The first term of an arithmetic sequence is 1 and the last term in the sequence is 29. If $s_n = 120$ find the number of terms in the sequence and the common difference.

Solution: Substitute $a_1 = 1$, $a_n = 29$ and $s_n = 120$ into

$$s_n = \frac{n(a_1 + a_n)}{2}$$

$120 = \frac{n(1 + 29)}{2}$ Substitution

$120 = \frac{30n}{2}$ Combine like terms

$120 = 15n$ Simplify

$6 = n$ Division property

Exercise Set 12.2

Write the first five terms and the expression for the nth term of the arithmetic sequence with the given first term and common difference.

1.) $a_1 = 5$ and $d = 7$.

2.) $a_1 = -47$ and $d = -8$.

Find the desired quantity in the arithmetic sequence.

3.) $a_1 = 205$, $d = 7$; find a_{10}.

4.) $a_1 = -10$, $a_{15} = -3$; find d.

-312-

Find the sum, s_n and the common difference d by completing the problem.

5.) $a_1 = 7$, $a_n = 49$ and $n = 12$

To find the sum, s_n:

$$s_n = \frac{n(a_1 + a_n)}{2}$$

$s_n = \dfrac{12(7 + ?)}{2}$ Substitution

$s_n = \dfrac{12(?)}{2}$ Combine like terms

$s_n = 6(?)$ Simplify

$s_n = ?$ Division property

To find the common difference, **d**.

$$a_n = a_1 + (n - 1)d$$

$49 = ? + (12 - 1)d$ Substitution

$49 = ? + 11d$ Combine like terms

$? = 11d$ Additive property

$? = d$ Division property

6.) Find the number of terms in the arithmetic sequence 18, 31, 44, ..., 148.

Solution to Exercise Set 12.2

1.) 5, 12, 19, 26, 33   2.) −47, −55, −63, −71, −79

3.) 151   4.) 1/2

5.) 336, 42/11   6.) 11

Section 12.3 Geometric Sequences and Series

Example 1. Find the seventh term of a geometric sequence whose first term is 17 and whose common ratio is 3.

Solution: Substitute $a_1 = 17$, $r = 3$ and $n = 7$ into:

$$a_1 = ar^{n-1}$$

$$a_7 = 17(3)^{7-1}$$

$$a_7 = 17(3)^6$$

$$a_7 = 17(729)$$

$$a_7 = 12393$$

Example 2. Find the common ratio for the geometric sequence with $a_3 = 12$ and $a_6 = 96$.

Solution: Assume 12 is the first term and 96 is the fourth term of a geometric sequence with the same common ratio.

$a_n = a_1 r^{n-1}$ n^{th} term of geometric sequence

$a_4 = a_1 r^{4-1}$ Substitute $n = 4$

$96 = 12r^3$ Substitute $a_1 = 12$ and $a_4 = 96$

$8 = r^3$ Division property

$2 = r$ Cubic root of both sides of the equation.